# The Chemist at work

CYRIL PARSONS, B.Sc. CLARE DOVER, B.Sc.

FOUNDATIONS OF SCIENCE LIBRARY

GREYSTONE PRESS/NEW YORK · TORONTO · LONDON

This new presentation assembles freshly edited material from
'Understanding Science' on one subject into a single volume.

Copyright © MCMLXVI Sampson Low, Marston & Co. Ltd.

Library of Congress Catalog Card Number: 66–17995

Printed in Great Britain
Manufactured in U.S.A.

F.S.C.W.—A

# Contents

# Laboratory Equipment
# and Procedure

# CHAPTER ONE

# Accurate Weighing

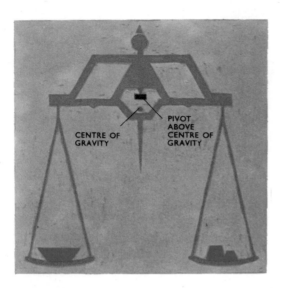

*If the beam were pivoted about its centre of gravity, the beam could be inclined at any angle and still be in equilibrium. The pivot is, therefore, above the centre of gravity so the beam is horizontal when there are equal masses on the two pans.*

MEASUREMENT of *weight*, or, to be more precise, *mass*, can reach a very high degree of accuracy, (over one part in a million with some really good balances). But no matter how much thought and skilled craftsmanship has gone into the construction of a precision balance, the readings may be valueless if the user is not sufficiently careful.

The chemical balance is one of the most important pieces of apparatus used by the analyst. It is particularly valuable when he wants to find the proportion of an impurity present as only a very small fraction of the total weight of the sample. In these circumstances more than in any others, great care must be exercised in the use of the balance. Errors could be introduced which are larger than the mass being measured. For instance an error of 0·001 gm. is not serious when weighing something whose mass is 100 gm. It would, however, be futile trying to detect a difference in mass of 0·001 gm. on the same balance.

The vast majority of chemical balances depend upon the *principle of moments*. Two identical scale pans hang from a uniform beam which is pivoted at its mid-point. The two pans hang from points on either side of the pivot and are the same distance from it. The beam is designed and loaded so that it is horizontal when *equal masses* are placed in the two pans. However, the balance can be affected by a number of external factors which are likely to upset equilibrium because they act on one part of the balance more than another.

Since a precision balance is itself expensive it is only reasonable that it should be properly housed. It is inevitable, in many chemical laboratories, that the atmosphere is contaminated with corrosive fumes which could, in time, eat into the metal parts of the balance making the masses of the scale pans unequal. The air may also contain water vapour which could condense on the beam and pans and upset their own masses.

On account of these and other difficulties it is now common practice to have a separate balance room which is used for nothing more than weighing. In some modern laboratories, balance rooms have been specially

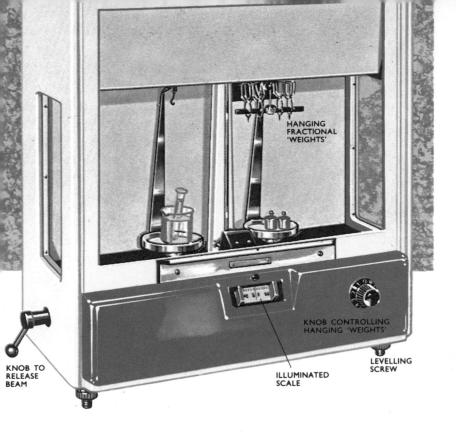

HANGING
FRACTIONAL
'WEIGHTS'

KNOB CONTROLLING
HANGING 'WEIGHTS'

KNOB TO
RELEASE
BEAM

ILLUMINATED
SCALE

LEVELLING
SCREW

*A precision balance capable of weighing to an accuracy of 0.0001 gm. The knob on the front of the balance case controls the hanging fractional 'weights'. The pulley mechanism which controls these 'weights' is shown in the foreground of the cut-away picture (below). The illuminated scale on the front of the balance has a range of 0·1 gm. (each division corresponding to 0·0002 gm). The lamp which illuminates the actual scale on the balance pointer is prominent in the cut-away picture.*

constructed so that the temperature and humidity are carefully controlled and the various other sources of error outlined below are reduced to a minimum. But in all the laboratories the humidity in the balance case itself can be kept low by using a drying agent such as silica gel. A dish or specially packed cartridge is placed in the corner of the case. Its drying ability can be restored periodically by heating in an oven at about 105°C.

Draughts can have quite serious effects on the accuracy of a weighing. The doors of the balance case, which can usually be closed while the weighing is being carried out, may afford sufficient protection. In general, this is true, but uneven temperatures in the balance case, such as those produced if a hot object is being weighed, can create air currents which lead to quite large errors. Any objects that have been heated must be allowed to cool in a desiccator before they are

weighed.

More accurate balances are quite sensitive to external vibrations. People

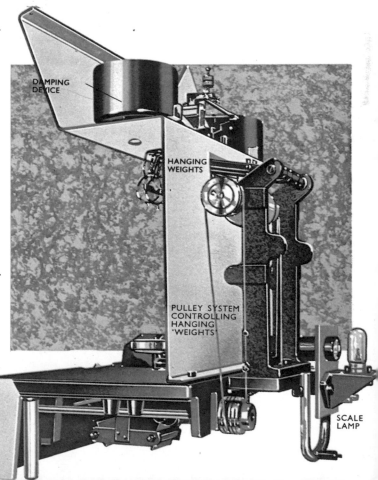

DAMPING
DEVICE

HANGING
WEIGHTS

PULLEY SYSTEM
CONTROLLING
HANGING
'WEIGHTS'

SCALE
LAMP

7

walking around the balance room or closing adjacent doors will often cause irregular motion of the balance beam. One way of reducing this effect is to support the balance on a firm base which is subject to the minimum of vibration. Balances are often placed on slabs of concrete or marble instead of wooden benches. It is most satisfactory if the slabs are let into an external wall, or in a ground floor laboratory they may be supported directly by the foundations.

The majority of balances will work well only if they are properly levelled (i.e. the base is horizontal and the central pillar is vertical). Levelling screws are provided to achieve this. Each time the balance is used, the level should be checked by reference to the incorporated plumb line or spirit level.

Some chemical substances may appear to be harmless, but even if a substance is not corrosive, it may be abrasive and slight scratching of the scale pan will affect its weight. All substances to be weighed should, therefore, be placed in a previously weighed dish or bottle. There are special bottles for weighing corrosive or volatile liquids. Should any substance fall on the scale pan it must be cleaned off immediately.

To make the best use of the balance and make it last longer all weighings need to be performed smoothly. There is certainly no place for the hasty operator in the balance room though, with care, weighing may be obtained quite rapidly. When the balance is not in use, the beam and scale pans are locked in one position to stop the pans from swinging, and must be released before an object can be weighed.

This has to be done as smoothly as possible. Not only does it enable the mass to be measured more rapidly (because the pans are not swinging), it also makes the pivots last longer. A good balance usually has a knife edge of agate (a form of naturally occurring silica) or synthetic sapphire (pure corundum) as the fulcrum. This is supported on a perfectly flat plate. Sudden movement of the beam can easily cause the surface to become chipped or the knife-edge rounded, so instead the beam slides about on a rounded surface.

To prevent unnecessary damage to these parts, the movement of the balance should always be arrested each time any object or 'weight' is placed on the pan or taken off. This can easily be overlooked when using the kind of balance where the smaller ('fractional') 'weights', are added by remote control. In this arrangement the 'weights' are loops of wire which can be added or taken from the right scale pan by turning a knob.

As well as eliminating the handling of the 'weights' and the risk of dropping them on the floor, such systems also make for more rapid results. Some balances of this type are capable of reading to $0 \cdot 1$ mgm ($0 \cdot 0001$ gm). The last two or three figures of the reading are frequently found by measuring the inclination of the beam to the horizontal by optical means.

At one time, accurate measurement of weight using a chemical balance was very time-consuming, for the sensitive apparatus came to rest only slowly. However, modern balances have special clamping devices incorporated in their design so that rapid measurements may be made without loss of accuracy.

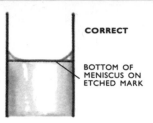

CORRECT

BOTTOM OF
MENISCUS ON
ETCHED MARK

WRONG

TOP OF
MENISCUS
ON ETCHED
MARK

## Measuring Liquids

The surface of a liquid close to the sides of the container is usually curved. This is known as the *meniscus* and for water and solutions of substances in water the lowest point of the meniscus is in the middle. When using a pipette or burette to measure volumes the *bottom* of the meniscus must be opposite the calibration mark which is etched on the sides of the tube.

CHAPTER TWO

# Measuring Liquids

THERE are many occasions when the scientist needs to know accurately the quantity of a substance which he is using or has produced in an experiment. The *weight* of a substance can be measured most accurately, but to weigh a sample takes time. Nevertheless weighing is used, almost without exception, as a means of finding how much solid is consumed.

Liquids can also be weighed, but unless a very accurate measurement is required, it is both easier and quicker to measure *volume*. The weight of liquid can be calculated from the volume, or the volume needed from the weight, since for a particular liquid these two quantities are related to one another by its density. As almost all liquids expand when they are heated, allowance has to be made for the resultant slight reduction in density at higher temperatures.

There are four different types of vessel for measuring liquid volumes, each type being suitable for particular jobs. *Measuring cylinders*, for instance, are used for approximate measurements either of the amount of liquid product obtained from a chemical reaction or of the quantity of liquid to be used in an experiment.

The scale on the side of a measuring cylinder is usually divided up into 100 equal parts. For instance a 100 ml. (ml. is the abbreviation used for millilitre) cylinder measures to the nearest 1 ml., while there is 5 ml. between each scale division of a 500 ml. cylinder. In view of the errors which can arise through using a large vessel for measuring a small volume (i.e. 9 ml. in a 100 ml. cylinder) some manufacturers do not mark in the first 10 units on the scale (i.e. the first 10 ml. on a 100 ml. cylinder).

However, if the volume of liquid to be used in an experiment has to be measured more accurately, it can be done with a pipette or burette. A *pipette* is a narrow tube into which the liquid is drawn by suction. In all but the smallest sizes there is a bulb part way up the tube. In this way most of the liquid is accommodated in the bulb, while the single calibration mark is located in the narrow stem, so ensuring an accurate measurement. A pipette is, therefore, used to deliver definite volumes (e.g. 10 ml., 25 ml.) which have been measured accurately.

There are, of course, instances in which odd volumes have to be measured out accurately, or it is required to know exactly how much liquid has been added in bringing a chemical reaction to completion. The *burette* has been designed to fulfil these needs. It consists of a long graduated tube with a tap at its lower end. Burettes are made in several sizes but the ones most frequently used hold 50

ml., and are subdivided into 0·1 ml. units. In use, the burette is filled to the zero mark at the top of the scale and then the required amount of liquid is run out through the tap. The volume taken is easily seen from the scale.

It must be emphasised, however, that both pipettes and burettes are intended to *deliver* certain stated volumes, provided the correct procedure is used each time. A certain amount of adhesion of liquid to the walls is inevitable but account will have been taken of this when the instrument was calibrated.

In contrast, *measuring flasks* are designed to *hold* the stated volume, since their principal use is in preparing solutions of known concentration such as may be required in volumetric analysis. To do this, a carefully weighed amount of powdered solid is dissolved in distilled water (or other solvent). Once the solid has dissolved, more water is added slowly until the calibration mark is reached.

Pipettes and burettes as well as measuring flasks are the tools of volumetric analysis. In this analytical technique, reactions are carried out in solution. The concentration of a solution may be determined by finding how much of it is required to neutralize a certain volume of another solution of known concentration.

# CHAPTER THREE

# Heating Things in the Laboratory

THE Bunsen burner is the most common source of heat. If a small quantity of liquid needs warming or boiling, this can be done by putting it in a test tube and slowly moving it in a roaring Bunsen flame. Moving the tube around keeps the liquid stirred and prevents the liquid from rocketing out of the tube. As the top of the test tube tends to become rather hot, it is best to hold the tube with a test tube holder.

Beakers of liquids are placed on tripods and gauze above the flame. The gauze helps to spread the heat evenly over the base of the beaker. The liquid can be stirred from time to time or a few pieces of porous pot can be added to prevent the liquid from making bumping noises and splashing out of the vessel.

This is fairly straight-forward and most liquids that have to be heated are heated this way. For some chemicals though, use of a direct flame can have distinct disadvantages. A direct flame will never produce an even heating. Different parts of the flame are at dissimilar temperatures.

A water bath is a much more even form of heating. The test tube or flask can be surrounded by boiling water or water at any other specified temperature. Keeping the temperature at 100°C presents no problems – just keep the water boiling. For lower temperatures, it is best to use a thermostatically controlled bath. The water-heater switches itself off when the temperature is likely to rise too high and comes on again when the temperature has dropped too far. Thermostatic water baths can be used to keep

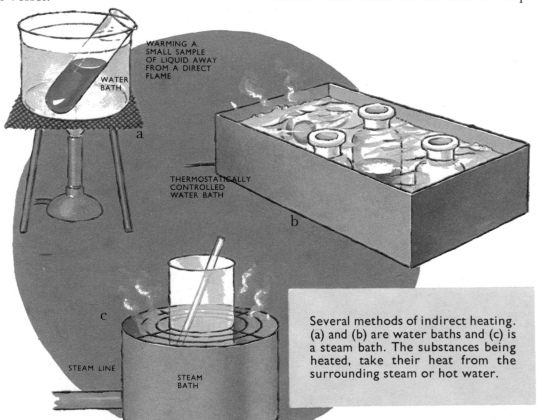

WARMING A SMALL SAMPLE OF LIQUID AWAY FROM A DIRECT FLAME

WATER BATH

a

THERMOSTATICALLY CONTROLLED WATER BATH

b

c

STEAM LINE

STEAM BATH

Several methods of indirect heating. (a) and (b) are water baths and (c) is a steam bath. The substances being heated, take their heat from the surrounding steam or hot water.

bottles and jars at a constant temperature for hours, days, or even weeks.

A further advantage of using a water bath is that the substance being heated is isolated from the direct flame. Anyone who tries to heat a test tube of benzene or toluene by holding it in a direct flame stands a good chance of getting burnt or starting a fire. These liquids are extremely inflammable and should be kept well clear of open flames. Not only should they be heated on an electrically operated water bath, but the Bunsen burners roundabout should also be extinguished as the vapours of these substances are also likely to catch fire. This rule applies to many organic substances.

Many laboratories have a steam pipeline leading to steam baths, which are just pans with lids made of metal rings. One or more rings can be removed, leaving a circular hole in the top, or more, leaving a larger hole. In a chemical laboratory, the main use of steam baths is in gravimetric analysis, analysis by weight. A metal which has been brought out of solution as an insoluble compound has to be filtered out, dried and weighed. Very often the crystals are small and are in danger of passing through the filter and being lost. Leaving the beaker to stand on a steam bath for several hours can help the crystals to grow in size. With the precipitate in a more granular condition the analytical results will probably be better.

Unless it is put under pressure, water will only give temperatures up to 100°C. It would not make sense to use pressure vessels when there are liquids with higher boiling points than water. For temperatures of more than 100°C, the heating is done in an oil bath. The effect is that of a chip pan – even heating for temperatures well

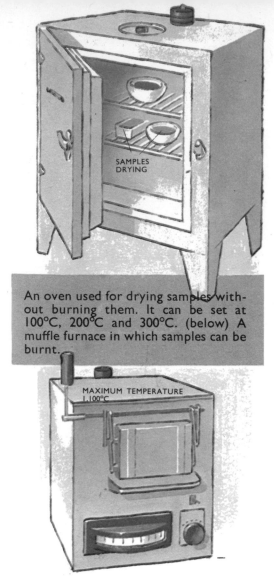

An oven used for drying samples without burning them. It can be set at 100°C, 200°C and 300°C. (below) A muffle furnace in which samples can be burnt.

above 100°C.

Oil baths are used for finding the melting points of many solids. A tiny sample of the solid in a capillary tube is gradually warmed in an oil bath. The temperature at which the solid suddenly collapses to a liquid is its melting point.

Oil can be messy to use. In preparing many organic substances, the round bottomed flask is embedded in hot sand – a *sand bath*. There is the additional advantage that the sand will absorb the liquid if the flask happens to crack.

Like kitchens, most laboratories also have their ovens. Some can be regulated to fairly low temperatures for growing moulds and bacteria. There are ovens where the humidity and temperature can be regulated. Ovens like this can be made to imitate a particular climate and used to test how things will behave under these conditions.

To dry out a wet precipitate, a dry oven will probably be set to just over 100°C. It is common practice to use an oven to obtain completely dry chemicals without burning them. Burning has to be done at a higher temperature still in a *muffle furnace*.

The drying ovens are largely used for completely driving off all the water from samples which are to be weighed as part of some analytical work. If any water is left behind, the analysis will give very poor results. It is no use raising the temperature too much because the samples may char and oxidize. This would be just as bad for the analysis. The wet substances are therefore left in the oven for as long as possible. It may be for several days, or at the minimum overnight. There is a special draught arrangement in the ovens to carry the water vapour away and prevent it from condensing again.

With long drying periods, fairly large ovens are needed as there will be several samples at different stages of drying in the oven. Some will be in porcelain evaporating dishes; others in porcelain filters and others in glass filters. It is quite all right to put glass vessels in a thermostatically controlled drying oven. The temperature is not allowed to rise sufficiently to melt the glass.

Glassware should never be used in a muffle furnace or any other furnace. As the temperature rises, the glass melts and drips and spreads itself over the lining of the furnace. The molten glass will ruin any future experiments if it is not removed and it is extremely difficult to remove.

The actual heating space in a furnace is much smaller than in an oven because it is usual to burn samples one at a time. The samples are often wrapped in ash-free paper to prevent some of them from being wafted away as fumes. The paper protects the sample in the early stages of the charring, but leaves no unwanted ash once it has burned.

CHAPTER FOUR

# Flame

FLAMES occasionally flicker and dance over the surface of a burning coal fire, but most of the time the fire is flameless, illuminated only by the red glow of burning solids. The flames leaping from it are areas in which gases are burning. When they burn, these gases combine with the oxygen of the air and in doing so, heat and light are given out making the flame hot and often visible.

If a gas will burn, then it always burns with a flame. For example, the gases carbon monoxide and hydrogen always burn with flames, carbon monoxide with a bright blue flame and hydrogen with a paler blue flame. But there is no hard and fast rule for *solids*. Some burn with flames; others do not. When some hot iron filings are lowered into a jar of oxygen, they burn with a dull red glow, but not with a flame. In

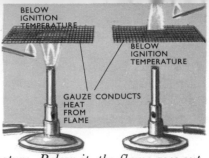

*Gases can only burst into flame above the ignition temperature. Below it, the flame goes out.*

contrast, under similar conditions, warm yellow phosphorus will burst into flame and cannot be made to burn flamelessly. If the temperature is raised sufficiently for some of the solid to vaporize, it burns with a flame as the vapour catches fire. If no vapour is given off then there can be no flame. Volatile substances burn more often with flames than non-volatile substances.

Before any gas or vapour can burst into flame a certain temperature must be reached. The lowest temperature at which the substance will take fire is known as the *ignition temperature*. The ignition temperature is not a fixed value for a particular gas for it varies with the conditions. Gas pressure and the presence of catalysts can affect it. At very low pressures, gases are made

*Arrows show gas movements in the different mantles of a roaring Bunsen flame.*

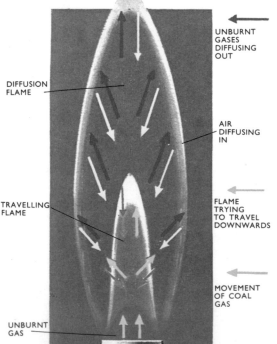

DIFFUSION FLAME

UNBURNT GASES DIFFUSING OUT

AIR DIFFUSING IN

TRAVELLING FLAME

FLAME TRYING TO TRAVEL DOWNWARDS

MOVEMENT OF COAL GAS

UNBURNT GAS

more difficult to set alight because the ignition temperature is much higher. For inflammable liquids this temperature is known as the *flash point*. It is the lowest temperature at which the liquid gives off a vapour that will burst into flame.

Whenever a temperature drops below the ignition temperature then the flame goes out. This is the theory behind putting a bucket of water on a fire to extinguish it. The water takes heat from the fire to raise its temperature and convert itself into steam. The fire loses heat and its temperature drops to below the ignition point. The flame dies.

When a piece of metal gauze is held above a Bunsen burner and a lighted taper is applied below, the flame formed has no tip. The flame is stopped by the gauze because the metal conducts heat away, preventing the gas above from reaching the ignition point and so it cannot catch fire. When the experiment is repeated, this time by applying the flame above the gauze, for the same reason, only the gas above the gauze catches fire. There is no flame, only unburnt gas beneath it.

Flames differ in appearance. There are several reasons for this. The flames may have different *structures*. Apart from at the centre, a candle flame appears uniformly yellow throughout; so does a luminous Bunsen flame, whereas a roaring Bunsen flame has an inner blue cone surrounded by an outer transparent cone. All flames also have a central zone of unburnt gas at

14

the base. This is quite easily demonstrated by holding a piece of asbestos paper so that it cuts across the lower part of the flame. A hollow ring of soot is deposited by the burning gas or vapour but none by the unburnt gases. Holding another piece of asbestos paper vertically in the flame shows the zone of unburnt gases to be cone-shaped.

The candle flame and the outer cone of the Bunsen flame are both examples of *diffusion flames*. When the candle is lit, the vaporized paraffin wax diffuses out from the wick and mingles with the air needed for its combustion. The gases which have been only partly burnt in the inner cone of the Bunsen flame behave similarly, diffusing out to mix with the inward diffusing air.

The inner Bunsen cone is an *explosion* or travelling flame. If a match is applied to one end of a tube of coal gas, the gas catches fire at that end and the flame travels along the tube, as each successive layer of gas is burnt.

The blue cone is a flame of this type, only the gas issuing from the Bunsen is not stationary. The rate at which the flame travels down through the gas is balanced by the rate at which more gas issues from the burner to take its place. As the two balance, the flame appears to be stationary. The travelling nature of the flame can be further demonstrated by turning down the gas supply. Then the flame travels down into the burner faster than the gas can come out and the Bunsen lights at the bottom. This is known as *striking back*. The Bunsen should never be left to burn with this sort of flame as the bottom of the burner becomes overheated. Also the gas is only partially burned and poisonous gases escape into the atmosphere.

## Cool Flames

The mind automatically associates flames with heat, but some are actually quite cool. Over a pressure range, particular mixtures of vapour and air give flames which are comparatively cool, with temperatures around 300° C. compared with normal flame temperatures of over 1,000° C.

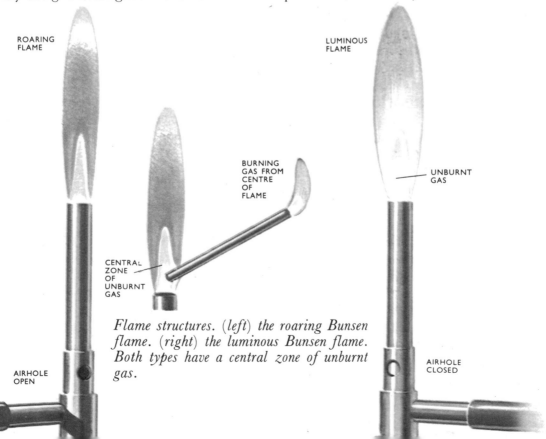

ROARING
FLAME

BURNING
GAS FROM
CENTRE
OF
FLAME

CENTRAL
ZONE
OF
UNBURNT
GAS

AIRHOLE
OPEN

LUMINOUS
FLAME

UNBURNT
GAS

AIRHOLE
CLOSED

*Flame structures. (left) the roaring Bunsen flame. (right) the luminous Bunsen flame. Both types have a central zone of unburnt gas.*

with cork or rubber which must be tightened with care to avoid cracking the glass. A tapered and curved tube called an adapter is placed over the lower end of the condenser held firmly on by a cork. A conical flask to collect the condensed vapour is placed so that the end of the adapter comes just inside its neck.

All the apparatus, the round bottomed flask, condenser, adapter and conical flask must be thoroughly washed and dried before assembling it. All corks must fit perfectly to prevent the escape of any vapour— this is particularly important when an inflammable mixture is being distilled. The side arm of the flask must be inserted into the neck of the condenser in the correct position so that there is no undue strain on the side arm. The cold water must enter the jacket of the condenser at the lower end so that the whole of the jacket is filled and thus cooling the whole of the inner tube. The flow of water need only be slow. If water entered the jacket from the top it would flow straight out through the bottom opening without cooling the inner tube.

A *water jacket* B *water inlet* C *water outlet* D *flask* E *side arm* F *adapter* G *receiver* H *clamp* I *stand* J *wire gauze* K *tripod* L *vapour.*

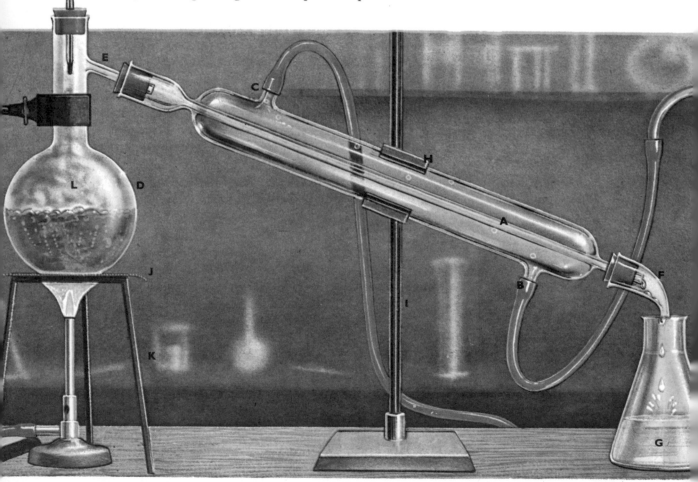

# Theory and Practice of

# Purification in the Laboratory

# CHAPTER SEVEN

# Solutions

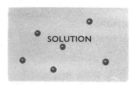
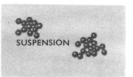

*In a* solution *the molecules of dissolved substance are distributed evenly throughout the solution whereas in a* suspension *they are not.*

A LIQUID with other substances *dissolved* in it is called a solution. Such mixtures are of great importance in the living world. For example the digested foods of human beings and other animals are carried in the form of solutions to all cells. Mineral salts occur as solutions in the soil and enter the roots of plants as solutions, passing to the farthest branches and leaves.

If a little sugar is added to water it gradually disappears from the bottom—this occurs more quickly if the mixture is stirred. Microscopic examination will not show any traces of sugar, but if the liquid is tasted it will be found to be sweet. The sugar has dissolved in the water, forming a *solution*. In doing so the molecules in the sugar crystals have separated from one another and become independent and evenly distributed throughout the water. A solution is a mixture which is *homogeneous* (which means identical throughout the whole) and, no matter how long this homogeneous mixture is left, its constituents will never separate. Solutions are always clear, although they may be coloured if the dissolved substance has a colour. The liquid (in this case water) which does the dissolving is called the *solvent*, and the substance dissolved is called the *solute*.

Water is also able to hold substances in *suspension*. The solid material in a suspension is not broken down into individual molecules—the particles are very much bigger. They make the water cloudy, whereas the particles in a solution are invisible, and in time the materials in suspension will settle out to the bottom. They can also be removed by sufficiently fine filters. Dissolved substances remain in solution indefinitely and cannot be filtered out. If chalk powder is shaken with water a milky suspension is formed. The particles are spread throughout the liquid but are *not* dissolved, for they will settle to the bottom in time. Some medicines are suspensions and we are told to

Glucose dissolves in water. It is impossible to see the glucose in the water.

The water has dissolved as much salt as it can. It is now a saturated solution. The salt which cannot dissolve remains at the bottom.

Solutions will pass through a filter whereas solid particles which are suspended in the solution will not.

shake the bottle before use. If a suspension of muddy or chalky water is poured through a fine filter, the water molecules pass through the pores of the filter, but the bigger suspended particles remain behind. This process is called *filtration*. The liquid coming through the filter is called the *filtrate* and the solids held back are called *residues*.

Substances in solution must be removed in other ways. On many occasions water as pure as possible is needed particularly in chemical analysis. Tap water would not do. It is not pure in a scientific sense, for it contains dissolved substances. Such water is evaporated and the steam is condensed by cooling. This process is known as *distillation* and the product is called distilled water. The dissolved substances are left behind when the water is evaporated and so are separated from it. In Nature, water evaporating from the oceans leaves the salts behind. Clouds are formed eventually and, later, rain may fall. Rain is 'fairly pure' water apart from gases of the air dissolved in it.

Another of Nature's ways of removing dissolved substances is by the formation of ice. When a solution of salt freezes, for example, ice crystals separate, leaving the dissolved substances behind in the unfrozen water. Eskimos who live where there is no fresh water are able to melt the ice formed from salt water to obtain water free from salt.

It is difficult to prepare *absolutely pure water*. Even distilled water is not perfectly pure for it even dissolves minute amounts of glass from its container which can prove a nuisance in the most delicate chemical research. It also contains dissolved gases from the air. Water is the commonest solvent. It is the 'best mixer' and indeed has been called the universal solvent because so many substances dissolve in it—some very readily. Even the so-called *insoluble* substances such as glass or chalk or sand dissolve in very minute amounts which are undetectable except by the most sensitive experiments. A solution of a substance in water is called an *aqueous* solution.

*The solvent can be recovered from a solution by distillation. Here water is being recovered from a blue solution of copper sulphate.*

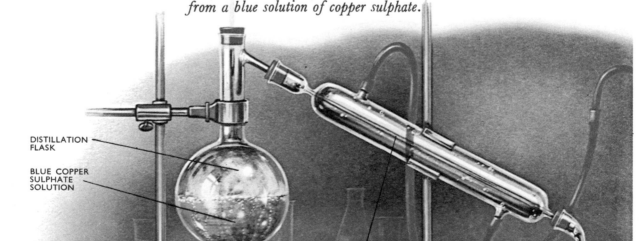

DISTILLATION FLASK

BLUE COPPER SULPHATE SOLUTION

CONDENSER

PURE WATER COLLECTS

There is a limit to the amount of a substance which can be dissolved in a given quantity of water. If a small amount of common salt is added to water and stirred, salt solution is formed. Further quantities can be dissolved, but eventually a stage is reached when no more salt will go into solution. The solution is then said to be *saturated*. If the water is heated, more salt will dissolve, but this extra amount will be thrown out of solution (i.e., it will crystallize) on cooling to the original temperature. Generally speaking the solubility of a solid increases as the temperature increases. Only a certain amount of solid can be held in a given amount of water at any given temperature. *Solubility* is usually defined as the weight (grams) of solute (dissolved substance) required to saturate 100 grams of water at a particular temperature.

In addition to solids dissolving in water, liquids and gases will form solutions also. Some gases, like ammonia, are extremely soluble in water. Ammonia gas forms ammonia solution used in the laboratory and the household (where it is known as "household ammonia"). Unlike solids, gases are more soluble in cold water than in hot water. Air can be shown to be soluble by raising the temperature of water when bubbles of air are driven out of solution. Dissolved atmospheric oxygen is responsible for the rusting of iron, and it also is of great biological importance. Fish and other water creatures depend upon the presence of *dissolved* oxygen in water. They extract the oxygen in order to live and when they have used up all the dissolved oxygen they will die—they cannot obtain the *combined* oxygen in water molecules by splitting up water. Hot water holds less oxygen than cold water, and so a fish bowl has to be changed more often in summer than in winter.

Gases under pressure dissolve more readily in water. Carbon dioxide is only slightly soluble in water, but if the gas is under pressure more will dissolve. When the pressure is released, the extra gas dissolved will bubble out of solution. "Mineral waters" and soda water contains carbon dioxide dissolved under pressure.

The solubility of gases increases with pressure. When the pressure is released the gas escapes; here carbon dioxide is escaping now that the cork has been removed from the bottle of lemonade.

A plant cell immersed in water swells because the cell sap is rich in sugar and salts. Its lining of protoplasm allows water to pass in, but prevents sugar from passing out. In strong salt solution the cell shrinks as its water passes out.

Water is by far the best solvent known and will dissolve more substances than any other liquid. It is itself inorganic (is not a carbon compound) and is a good solvent for other inorganic materials, but it will not dissolve oily and greasy substances which are organic compounds (compounds of carbon). To dissolve organic compounds, a compound which is itself organic is needed, so liquids such as carbon tetrachloride are used to dissolve them. Benzene will dissolve rubber, and alcohol will dissolve many substances—like iodine and shellac for varnishes. Amyl acetate, which smells like pear drops, will dissolve cellulose and is used for making lacquers and nail varnishes. Turpentine dissolves paint and is used for diluting it or for removing paint stains.

# CHAPTER EIGHT

# Colloids

COLLOIDS may be regarded as the stage between true solutions and coarse suspensions. In a true solution, the solute (the substance which is dissolved in the solvent) is broken up into separate molecules, which may in turn break up (dissociate) into ions. The separate molecules in a true solution are, of course, so small that they cannot be detected, even with the aid of the electron microscope. In contrast, the particles in a coarse suspension are sufficiently large, consisting as they do of many molecules each, that they may be removed from the suspension by filtration. Furthermore, the size of the particles in a suspension is such that even the finest particles will settle to the bottom of the container in a period of a few days, while the coarser particles settle out in a few minutes.

The properties of colloids lie between those of true solutions and of coarse suspensions. The colloidal particles are sufficiently large to be photographed using the electron microscope, but they are still small enough (about one million particles placed side by side measure 1 cm.) to remain in suspension indefinitely. Colloidal particles do not settle out of the dispersion, neither is there a filter fine enough to remove the colloidal particles from the solvent in which they are dispersed.

When a powerful beam of light is brought to a focus in a colloidal dispersion, and the focal point is observed through a powerful microscope which has been set up so that the microscope is perpendicular to the path of the beam, a large number of brilliant discs are seen. These discs are not still; they are forever dancing around in the solvent rather like mosquitoes in the air. This random

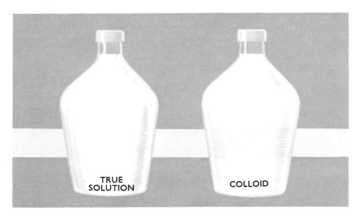 

*The path of the beam of light passing through the bottle on the right is visible because the colloidal particles reflect its rays. There is nothing to reflect light passing through the true solution (left). This is the Tyndall Effect. The arsenic sulphide solution in the U-tube tends to move towards the positive electrode when the current is switched on. This migration of colloids in an electric field is called electrophoresis.*

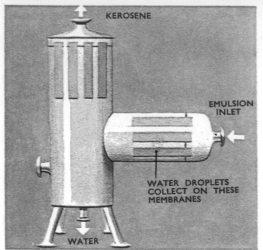

In an apparatus such as this a water-in-kerosene emulsion can be broken. The separate water droplets are brought together in it, and since water is denser than the kerosene, water can be withdrawn from the base.

motion of colloidal particles, which is caused by the solvent molecules hitting the dispersed particles unevenly, is referred to as *Brownian Movement*, since it was Robert Brown who first noticed this effect in 1828.

The substance which is dispersed (i.e. the solute) is often referred to as the *disperse phase*, while the solvent in which it is dispersed is known as the *dispersion medium* or more rarely the *continuous phase*.

Certain substances have the power to trap molecules of other materials on their surfaces. This property is known as *adsorption*. A large number of reactions such as the formation of ammonia from hydrogen and nitrogen will only occur at such surfaces, since the various reactants have first to be brought together by adsorption. It is thought that many catalysts are, in fact, adsorption agents, and since the surface areas of colloids are far greater than those of a corresponding weight of coarser particles catalysts are often used in the colloidal state.

CHAPTER NINE

# Solubility

SUGAR dissolves more easily in freshly poured tea than in a cup of tea which has been left standing for a while and has cooled. With many other solid substances, too, larger quantities will dissolve in a solvent when it is hot than when it is cold. Furthermore, at any one temperature, there is a great variation in the quantity of different substances which will dissolve in the same amount of a solvent.

A substance like potassium car-bonate is said to be very soluble in water because very many of its crystals have to be added to the water before no more will dissolve. When some of the crystals remain on the base of the container and will not dissolve even after a lapse of time, the solution is said to be *saturated*. In contrast, a saturated solution of a substance like calcium hydroxide (slaked lime) is obtained after only a few lumps are added to the water. Calcium hydroxide is, there-

## Solubility of Potassium Nitrate

| | |
|---|---|
| Temperature at which solution was saturated | 18°C |
| Wt. of clean, dry evaporating dish | = 32·05 gm |
| Wt. of dish + saturated solution | = 89·08 gm |
| Wt. of dish + dry salt | = 45·61 gm |
| Wt. of dry salt = (45·61 − 32·05) | = 13·56 gm |
| Wt. of water = (89·08 − 45·61) | = 43·47 gm |

43·47 gm of water dissolve 13·56 gm of the salt

1·00 gm of water dissolves $\frac{13·56}{43·47}$ gm of the salt

100 gm of water dissolve $\frac{13·56 \times 100}{43·47}$

$$= 31·2 \text{ gm of the salt}$$

Solubility of potassium nitrate in water at 18°C is

31·2 gm per 100 gm water.

MAKING A SATURATED SOLUTION

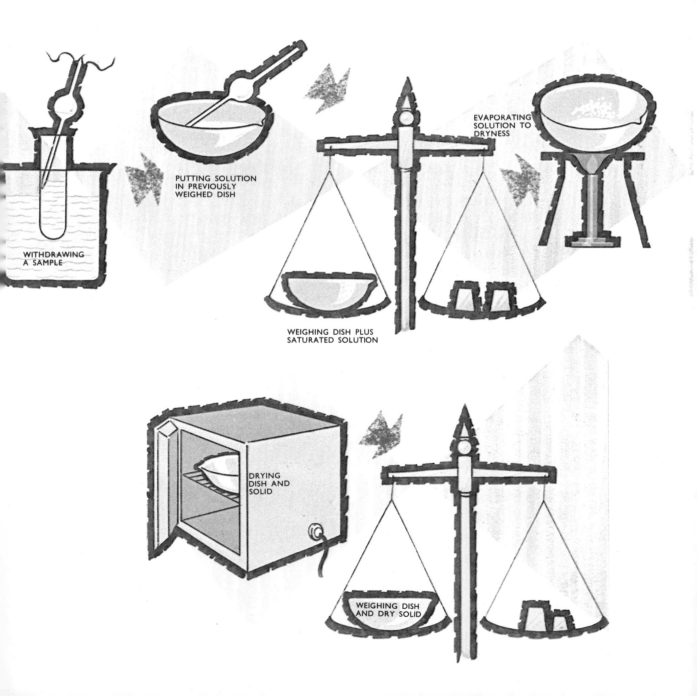

WITHDRAWING A SAMPLE

PUTTING SOLUTION IN PREVIOUSLY WEIGHED DISH

WEIGHING DISH PLUS SATURATED SOLUTION

EVAPORATING SOLUTION TO DRYNESS

DRYING DISH AND SOLID

WEIGHING DISH AND DRY SOLID

fore, only slightly soluble in water.

Although it may be sufficient, in many instances, to know that potassium carbonate is very soluble while calcium hydroxide is only slightly soluble, there are occasions where it is necessary to be more precise about the solubility of a substance. Chemists have, therefore, defined *solubility* as the number of grams of the substance (i.e. the solute) which at a specified temperature will dissolve in 100 gm. of the solvent to form a saturated solution.

Thus the first step in measuring the solubility of a solid is to make a saturated solution. This may, of course, be done by placing an excess of the substances in powder form into a flask, shaking it vigorously and then leaving it for a few days to finish dissolving. (The solid is reduced to powder since small particles dissolve more rapidly than large crystals).

There is, however, an alternative and quicker method of making a solution which will be saturated at a particular temperature. The solvent is heated until its temperature is well above the required level. Small portions of the powdered solid are stirred in until no more will dissolve (i.e. until

some of the powder remains on the bottom of the beaker some time after it was added). Then the solution is set aside to cool. If it is required that the solution shall be saturated at a temperature other than room temperature, it must be placed in a thermostatically controlled bath, which is maintained at the required temperature.

This method is, of course, only applicable to substances whose solubilities increase as the temperature of the solution is raised. Thus, as the solution cools it becomes more saturated. Once the solution is saturated, any further cooling should result in small crystals of the solute (i.e. the dissolved substance) being deposited. As cooling continues, the crystals grow because more of the solute is rejected from the solution. So the solution is saturated at any temperature below that at which crystals first started to form. But before a sample is withdrawn, time must be allowed for the solution to reach equilibrium. This applies particularly if the solution is being cooled, for all the solution must be at the same temperature and an opportunity must be provided for further crystals to be deposited.

Once the saturated solution has been made, all that remains is to find out how much of the solid is dissolved in a known weight of the solvent. A convenient way of doing this is to draw off into a pipette between 20 ml. and 30 ml. of the solution. Great care must be taken in using the pipette lest a few fine crystals are also withdrawn at the same time. (Alternatively the solution may be decanted to separate it from the deposit of crystals).

The contents of the pipette are then run into a previously weighed evaporating dish. The dish is weighed again

The solubilities of most solids increase as the solution temperature rises, so by heating the water more of the copper sulphate crystals dissolve.

COPPER
SULPHATE

after the solution has been added and then the solution is heated carefully so as to drive off the solvent. The final stages of the evaporation must be carried out cautiously, as many solids tend to spit when they are almost dry. The last traces of solvent are best removed by drying in an oven.

After the evaporating dish, which now contains only dry crystals of the solute, has cooled and been weighed, the dish may be heated again in the oven to see if all the solvent has been driven off. To be quite sure that the correct weight is recorded, the processes of heating, cooling and weighing should be repeated until two successive readings are the same.

From the sequence of weighings, the weight of solid and the *weight of pure solvent* (not the weight of solution) can be found. It is then fairly easy to calculate the solubility of the substance at that temperature.

The easiest way of depicting the variation in the solubility of a substance with temperature is to plot the information on a graph. Such graphs are known as *solubility curves*. To obtain the curve for one substance it may be necessary to determine its solubility at perhaps 5° intervals over the whole temperature range for which the solvent is a liquid. Once the curve has been plotted, the solubility at any temperature within the range may be read off.

Under normal circumstances, the maximum amount of solid that will dissolve in a solvent at a certain temperature is the amount necessary to yield a saturated solution. It is sometimes possible, however, to have a solution which contains rather more solute than is required to saturate it. Such a solution, which is unstable, is said to be *supersaturated*.

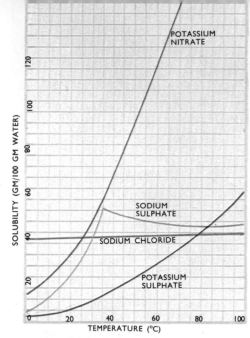

These curves show the variation with temperature of the solubilities of crystalline substances. Whereas the solubility of sodium chloride only increases slightly as the solution is heated, much more potassium nitrate will dissolve in hot water than in cold.

Supersaturation usually occurs when a hot solution which contains neither crystals of the solute nor dust is set aside to cool. The excess of solid may remain in solution so long as the solution is left undisturbed, and no dust is allowed to enter the container. However, once a tiny crystal of the solid is dropped into the solution, crystallization starts at once and continues until only sufficient solid to saturate the solvent remains in solution. Solutions of some solids (e.g. sodium thiosulphate or 'hypo') are particularly liable to become supersaturated, and it is for this reason that a few crystals should always be present in a vessel containing a saturated solution.

Both liquids and gases dissolve as well as solids. But whereas the solubilities of solids usually increase as the temperature of the solutions increase, the solubilities of gases fall off as the solvent is heated.

# CHAPTER TEN

# Solubility Product

## Law of Mass Action

This law can be applied to the equilibrium between undissociated molecules of solid in solution and the ions in solution. So if the molecule $AB$ dissociates to give $A^+$ and $B^-$ ions, according to the equation:

$$AB = A^+ + B^-$$

the equilibrium constant for this reaction is:

$$K = \frac{[A^+] \times [B^-]}{[AB]}$$

But as the concentration of undissociated solid is constant in a saturated solution, this equation may be rearranged:

$$[A^+] \times [B^-] = K[AB] = K_S$$

This new constant $K_S$ is the solubility product. So if the concentration of a univalent anion (e.g. chloride) is doubled in a solution of silver chloride, the concentration of the silver ions is halved.

THE system of analysis used for identifying the metallic ions present in a mixture of inorganic compounds depends upon the very low solubilities of certain salts of the metals. Silver, lead and mercurous ions are detected first because a precipitate of silver, lead or mercurous chloride is formed when hydrochloric acid is added to the solution. Then the metals whose sulphides are insoluble in acidic solutions are separated by passing hydrogen sulphide gas through the solution. So, in turn, all metals are separated into groups.

When salts are dissolved in water, and all of them dissolve, if only very slightly, some of the dissolved molecules divide up into ions. For example, each molecule of sodium sulphate

## Purification of Sodium Chloride

One of the most important applications of solubility product is in qualitative analysis. It can also be used in purifying a comparatively soluble substance. For instance sodium chloride may be purified by passing hydrogen chloride gas into a saturated solution of the salt. As the solution is already saturated, increasing the concentration (or active mass) of either sodium or chloride ions brings about crystallization. This is known as the *common ion* effect. So pure crystals of sodium chloride come out of solution leaving the impurities behind in the solution. Precipitation is not entirely due to the common ion effect.

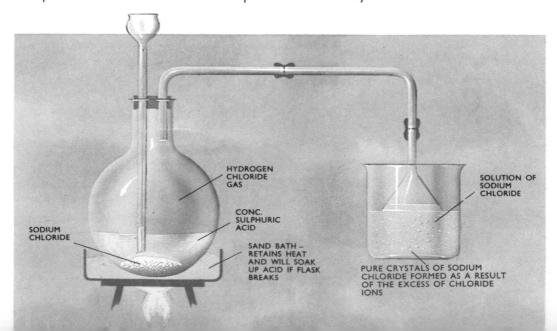

HYDROGEN CHLORIDE GAS

SOLUTION OF SODIUM CHLORIDE

CONC. SULPHURIC ACID

SODIUM CHLORIDE

SAND BATH – RETAINS HEAT AND WILL SOAK UP ACID IF FLASK BREAKS

PURE CRYSTALS OF SODIUM CHLORIDE FORMED AS A RESULT OF THE EXCESS OF CHLORIDE IONS

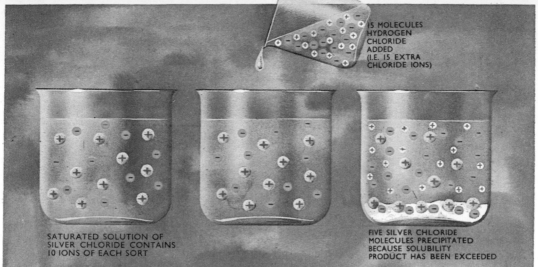

SATURATED SOLUTION OF SILVER CHLORIDE CONTAINS 10 IONS OF EACH SORT

15 MOLECULES HYDROGEN CHLORIDE ADDED (I.E. 15 EXTRA CHLORIDE IONS)

FIVE SILVER CHLORIDE MOLECULES PRECIPITATED BECAUSE SOLUBILITY PRODUCT HAS BEEN EXCEEDED

If, when a saturated solution of silver chloride is made in 1 litre of water, only 100 molecules ionize, the solubility product is $100 \times 100 = 10,000$ (100 silver ions and 100 chloride ions are produced). 150 molecules of hydrogen chloride (150 hydrogen and 150 chloride ions) are then added. This immediately raises the concentration of chloride ions to 250 and the product of silver and chloride ions to $250 \times 100 = 25,000$. As this is higher than the solubility product, some silver chloride comes out of solution so reducing the concentration of silver ions. If the volume of hydrochloric acid is neglected, precipitation will continue until 50 molecules of silver chloride have been removed – the concentration of silver and chloride ions in solution is then 50 and 200 respectively and the solubility product is again 10,000 ($50 \times 200$).

which ionizes yields two sodium ions (each with a single positive charge) and one sulphate ion with two negative charges. Molecules of silver chloride split up into equal numbers of silver ions (with single positive charge) and chloride ions with single negative charges.

Because they dissociate (split up) into ions, these substances are called *electrolytes*. With some electrolytes almost all the molecules split up into ions while only a few molecules of other electrolytes ionize in solution. A *strong* electrolyte is one which is largely dissociated into ions, while a *weak* electrolyte is one which is only slightly ionized in solution. Even some electrolytes which are only slightly soluble (e.g. lead chloride) dissociate to some considerable extent and rank as fairly strong electrolytes.

When a salt which is only slightly soluble has been in contact with water for some time, the water will have become saturated with the salt – no more of the salt will dissolve. But although

the concentration of the solution cannot increase at the particular temperature, some molecules of the salt will continue to pass into solution while an exactly equal number will crystallize out. Equilibrium will also exist between the dissolved molecules and the dissociated ions – no sooner has one molecule ionized than other ions come together to reform a molecule.

By applying the *law of mass action* to this equilibrium, it follows that the product of the concentrations of the ions produced when the solute molecules ionize will also be constant. This constant, which is, of course, dependent upon temperature, is called the *solubility product*. If, for any reason, the product of the ionic concentrations rises above this figure for the particular solution, precipitation will take place and will continue until the product has fallen to the original level.

One of the most important consequences of this is that the solubility product can be exceeded by increasing the concentration of either of the ions.

29

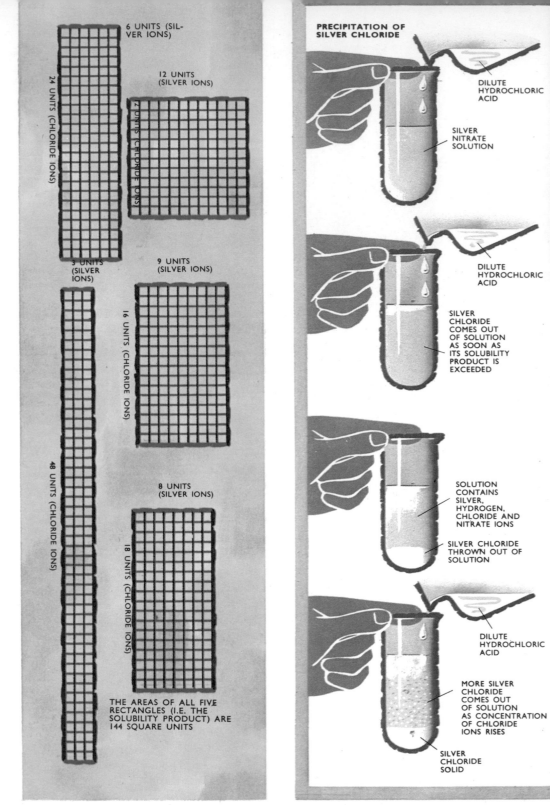

*If the concentration of the silver ions and the chloride ions in a saturated solution of silver chloride is represented by the vertical and horizontal sides respectively of a rectangle, the area of the rectangle represents the solubility product. This sequence of diagrams (left) shows how the concentration of silver ions gets less as the concentration of chloride ions is increased.*

Silver chloride can be thrown out of solution if the concentration of silver ions is increased by adding silver nitrate solution or if, by adding hydrochloric acid, the concentration of chloride ions is raised.

In qualitative analysis the systematic separation of the metallic ions into groups serves two purposes. It makes possible the identification of the metals within each group, and also removes the metallic ions group by group. Otherwise the identification of the ions in subsequent groups would be hindered by the presence of a few remaining from the previous groups.

It is of the utmost importance, therefore, that the Group I ions (silver, lead and mercurous) are removed as completely as possible before starting to test for the Group II ions. But the chlorides of silver, lead and mercurous mercury are all slightly soluble, so special precautions must be taken.

If, for instance, the original solution contained silver nitrate, the addition of a few drops of dilute hydrochloric acid will probably cause some silver chloride to be precipitated because the solubility product of this compound has been exceeded. However, there are still many silver ions in solution, and the addition of each extra drop of hydrochloric acid will cause more silver chloride to come out of solution. But even when the number of chloride ions in solution equals the number of silver ions, not all the silver chloride will have been precipitated. This can be remedied by adding more hydrogen chloride, since raising the concentration of chloride ions automatically reduces the concentration of silver ions.

It is because of this effect that in qualitative analysis the majority of reagents have to be added in excess. Otherwise small, but significant quantities of ions which should be completely removed previously remain in solution and upset the identification of other metallic ions in later groups.

CHAPTER ELEVEN

# Removing Impurities

IT is a fairly easy matter to separate the mixture of salt and sand because salt dissolves in water while sand does not. However, the separation of certain other mixtures is much more difficult. Methods which make use of differences in the physical properties (e.g. solubility, or boiling point) of the components of the mixture are generally preferred. But occasionally chemical means have to be used. For instance, the last few per cent of water in ethyl alcohol is usually removed by adding quicklime (calcium oxide) which reacts with the water to form slaked lime (calcium hydroxide). Pure (or *absolute*) alcohol is then distilled off.

The purity of a substance is normally tested by measuring its melting point or boiling point. Whereas pure substances always have quite definite melting and boiling points, the presence of impurities, even in quite small proportions, will affect the temperatures at which a substance melts or boils. In general, contaminated substances melt at temperatures below their normal melting points but boil at temperatures higher than the boiling point of the pure material.

MIXTURE OF CRYSTALS OF TWO SALTS DISSOLVED IN WATER

SOLUTION EVAPORATED SLOWLY

ONCE SOME CRYSTALS HAVE FORMED, THE DISH IS ALLOWED TO COOL

CRYSTALS (MAINLY OF LESS SOLUBLE SALT) COLLECT IN FILTER

EVEN BETTER SEPARATION IS POSSIBLE IF THE CRYSTALS ARE DISSOLVED AGAIN AND THE PROCESS REPEATED

SOLUTION RICHER IN MORE SOLUBLE SALT PASSES THROUGH FILTER

## Two Soluble Salts

It is more difficult to separate a mixture of two similar solids which dissolve in water than it is to separate salt and sand. However, it is unlikely that the solubilities of the two substances will be similar at all temperatures. Solubilities can be found from tables, and from this information a temperature is chosen where the solubilities of the two components are quite different. The solubilities of potassium sulphate and potassium nitrate are quite close at room temperature. At 70°C they are far apart. About 140 gm of potassium nitrate will dissolve in 100 gm water while only 33 gm of potassium sulphate dissolves in 100 gm water at the same temperature.

The mixture of these two salts is added to a flask of hot water and shaken until all the crystals have dissolved. This solution is then evaporated slowly and carefully. After a while crystals start to be deposited and it is found that the crystals are almost pure potassium sulphate (the less soluble component) while at the same time the solution becomes richer in potassium nitrate.

The potassium sulphate crystals are then filtered off. They will still contain some potassium nitrate as impurity. However, by dissolving the first crop of crystals, this new solution will yield much purer crystals of potassium sulphate.

The original solution of the mixed salts now contains a much higher proportion of potassium nitrate. The proportion can be further improved by continuing the evaporation.

Some liquids which do not dissolve in one another are found mixed together. However, if they are left to stand for a while in a separating funnel the two liquids separate out into two layers. The denser liquid can then be drained off through the tap in the stem of the funnel.

The separating funnel can also be used for extracting a solid or liquid from solution using another solvent. Many organic substances dissolve in ether more readily than they do in water, so that by shaking the aqueous solution with ether a large portion of the solute leaves the water and dissolves in ether. The mixture is left in the separating funnel so that the two liquids can separate into two layers. The watery layer is then run off leaving most of the substance in the ether. Shaking with several small portions of ether will remove most of the substance — more than if the same volume of ether had been used at one time.

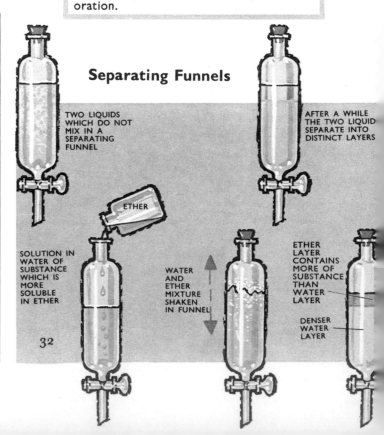

## Separating Funnels

TWO LIQUIDS WHICH DO NOT MIX IN A SEPARATING FUNNEL

AFTER A WHILE THE TWO LIQUID SEPARATE INTO DISTINCT LAYERS

ETHER

SOLUTION IN WATER OF SUBSTANCE WHICH IS MORE SOLUBLE IN ETHER

WATER AND ETHER MIXTURE SHAKEN IN FUNNEL

ETHER LAYER CONTAINS MORE OF SUBSTANCE THAN WATER LAYER

DENSER WATER LAYER

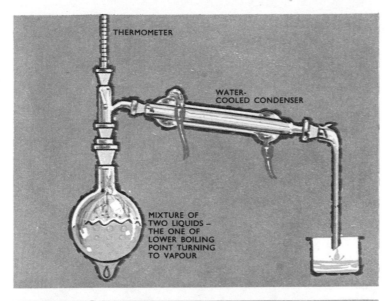

THERMOMETER

WATER-COOLED CONDENSER

MIXTURE OF TWO LIQUIDS – THE ONE OF LOWER BOILING POINT TURNING TO VAPOUR

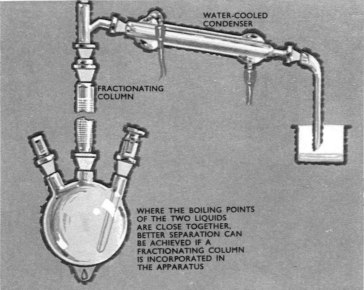

WATER-COOLED CONDENSER

FRACTIONATING COLUMN

WHERE THE BOILING POINTS OF THE TWO LIQUIDS ARE CLOSE TOGETHER, BETTER SEPARATION CAN BE ACHIEVED IF A FRACTIONATING COLUMN IS INCORPORATED IN THE APPARATUS

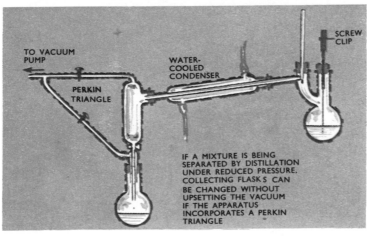

TO VACUUM PUMP

PERKIN TRIANGLE

WATER-COOLED CONDENSER

SCREW CLIP

IF A MIXTURE IS BEING SEPARATED BY DISTILLATION UNDER REDUCED PRESSURE, COLLECTING FLASKS CAN BE CHANGED WITHOUT UPSETTING THE VACUUM IF THE APPARATUS INCORPORATES A PERKIN TRIANGLE

## Distillation

The usual method for separating liquids, which are dissolved in one another, is to distil them. The mixture is placed in a flask which is heated, and provided the boiling points of the two liquids are not too close, quite good separation is obtained.

The liquid with the lower boiling point turns to vapour first, so in the beginning the vapour is more rich in the component with the lower boiling point. However, this vapour will contain some of the other component too. After most of the lower boiling point liquid has vaporized and passed into the condenser, the temperature of the remaining liquid rises quite suddenly and vapour of the liquid with the higher boiling point then comes over into the condenser.

Distillation is also used for separating the pure solvent from a solution of solids in the liquid. In this instance the liquid boils and its vapour is condensed, so leaving the solid behind in the distillation flask.

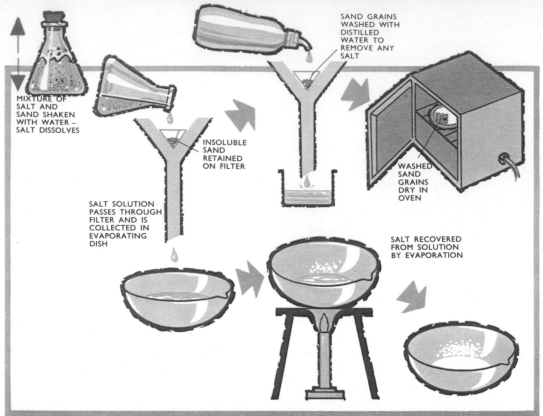

SAND GRAINS WASHED WITH DISTILLED WATER TO REMOVE ANY SALT

MIXTURE OF SALT AND SAND SHAKEN WITH WATER – SALT DISSOLVES

INSOLUBLE SAND RETAINED ON FILTER

SALT SOLUTION PASSES THROUGH FILTER AND IS COLLECTED IN EVAPORATING DISH

WASHED SAND GRAINS DRY IN OVEN

SALT RECOVERED FROM SOLUTION BY EVAPORATION

## Salt and Sand

If only one of two substances in a mixture dissolves in water (or in any other common solvent) they can be separated quite easily. The mixture (e.g. salt and sand) is put into a flask containing water and is shaken until all the salt has dissolved in the water. The contents of the flask are then poured into a cone of filter paper in a filter funnel. The salt solution passes through the filter while the sand is retained on the filter paper.

The filtrate which contains only salt can then be evaporated to recover the pure sodium chloride. There will, however, be some salt solution spread over the sand grains in the funnel. The sand grains must, therefore, be washed with water to remove the residual salt, before the pure sand is put aside to dry.

# CHAPTER TWELVE

# Filtration

QUITE frequently the chemist wishes to separate a powdered solid from the liquid in which it is suspended. For example, he may wish to collect the precipitated barium sulphate when analysing a sample to find the proportion of sulphate it contains. Similarly, in the *Solvay Process* for the manufacture of sodium carbonate, sodium bicarbonate powder has to be separated from ammonium chloride solution. Although there is a vast difference between the scale of these two processes, in each case the solid is separated from the liquid by *filtration*.

By passing the liquid through a porous material referred to as the *filter*, most of the solid particles suspended in the liquid may be collected. The filter may be regarded as a very fine sieve or strainer, and it is only the

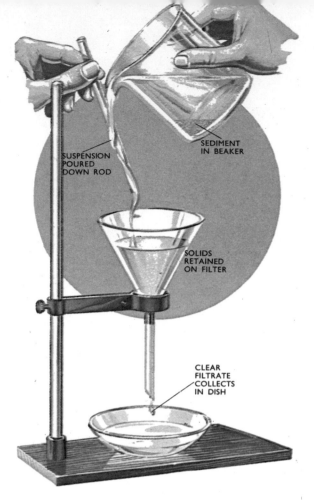

SUSPENSION POURED DOWN ROD

SEDIMENT IN BEAKER

SOLIDS RETAINED ON FILTER

CLEAR FILTRATE COLLECTS IN DISH

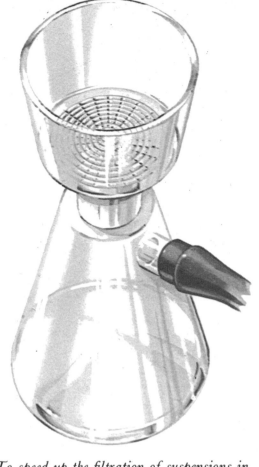

*In the laboratory many suspensions can be filtered satisfactorily through a cone of filter paper held in a filter funnel.*

clear liquid, or *filtrate* which passes through the filter.

A wide range of filter media is now available, and the choice for a particular application will depend on the size of particle to be removed and also upon the chemical properties of the filter. Clearly the material of which the filter or filter holder is made must not react with the liquid being filtered. The most frequently used types of filter incorporate various types of cloth or paper, but porous earthenware is also used occasionally.

In the laboratory, suspensions are usually filtered through specially prepared papers which have a similar texture to blotting paper. Circular

*To speed up the filtration of suspensions in the laboratory, the filtrate may be pulled through a Buchner filter by applying a vacuum.*

discs of this *filter paper* may be folded so as to fit into the conical filter funnel. (see illustrations). When filtering a suspension through one of these funnels the liquid is added in small quantities so that there is always some filter paper visible above the liquid level. The suspension should be poured into the centre of the filter, and if possible down a glass rod. This stops the particles in suspension trickling down the outside of the beaker and being lost. If the suspended solid is required pure, or if all the substances in solution are to be recovered, the material retained in the filter must be washed several times with the pure solvent.

Certain types of suspended particle tend to clog the pores of the filter and so slow down the rate of filtration. This is particularly true of suspensions in which the solid concentration is high. The flow rate through the filter may be increased by enlarging the filter area or by applying a vacuum to the clean side of the filter. In the laboratory these requirements may be achieved by using a *Buchner funnel*. In this, the circular disc of filter paper is used flat and is supported on a perforated platform which extends across the widest part of the funnel. The filtrate runs into a conical flask from which the air has been removed by a vacuum pump.

Filter paper is made in various qualities to suit different suspended solids and solvents, but not all suspensions met with in the laboratory can be filtered through paper. In such instances the chemist makes his own filter by packing a plug of glass wool or of asbestos fibre into a suitable small funnel.

When suspensions are to be filtered in the laboratory, the quantities involved are usually quite small, and in many instances the complete batch can be passed through a single disc of filter paper. Filtration in the laboratory is essentially a *batch process* – the whole of each batch is passed through the filter and only then is the solid residue recovered.

On the industrial scale there is a choice of equipment for both continuous and batchwise filtration. If the liquid which is to be filtered contains only a small portion of suspended solids it will probably be economic to regard filtration as a batch process. If a continuous output of liquid is required, two filters may be arranged in parallel, so that one can be dismantled and the solid removed while the second filter is 'on stream'.

CHAPTER THIRTEEN

# Partial Pressures

VALVE CLOSED

VALVE OPEN

PRESSURE OF NITROGEN – 101·9 cm Hg PLUS ATMOSPHERIC PRESSURE

VALVE OPEN

ALL FLASKS HAVE SAME VOLUME

NITROGEN PRESSURE 177·9 cm Hg

VALVE CLOSED

OXYGEN PRESSURE 48·0 cm Hg

VALVE CLOSED

ARGON PRESSURE – 2·1 cm Hg

ACCORDING to the Kinetic Theory, the pressure of a gas results from the collision of its molecules with the walls of the containing vessel. As air is a mixture of gases, the molecules of each gas contribute to the total pressure of the air.

The principal constituents of dry air are nitrogen (78% by volume), oxygen (21% by volume) and argon (1%); so there are many more nitrogen molecules than oxygen molecules striking the walls of a jar of air. In fact, the pressure produced at a fixed point by each type of molecule is directly proportional to the number of collisions and therefore to the number of molecules of each substance. For every 100 collisions of argon molecules with the wall, there will be 2,100 collisions of oxygen molecules and 7,800 collisions of nitrogen molecules with the wall.

The pressure contributed by the nitrogen molecules is called the *partial pressure* of the nitrogen in the air. Likewise, the partial pressure of oxygen is the pressure resulting from the oxygen molecules present in the mixture colliding with the walls. The total pressure of the air is the sum of the partial pressures of all the different gases in the air.

The law concerning the partial pressure exerted by the components of a mixture of gases had been deduced experimentally by John Dalton in 1801 well before it was justified by the Kinetic Theory. Known as *Dalton's Law of Partial Pressure*, it states that –

In any mixture of gases which do not react with one another, the total pressure of the mixture is the sum of the pressures (i.e. the partial pressures) which each gas would exert if it alone occupied the whole volume of the mixture, at the same temperature.

The truth of this law may be demonstrated quite simply by allowing measured volumes of different gases at known pressures to mix. For instance, air can be synthesized if three flasks having the same volume contain

(*Left*) *In an experiment to synthesize air, nitrogen, oxygen and argon are introduced into the three equal flasks, one gas in each. The pressure of these gases are arranged to be 177·9 cm, 48·0 cm and 2·1 cm Hg. (Below) When the valves of the three flasks are opened, the gases in them quickly mix by diffusion. The pressure of the mixture of gases is the same as that of the atmosphere, and has the same physical properties as dry air.*

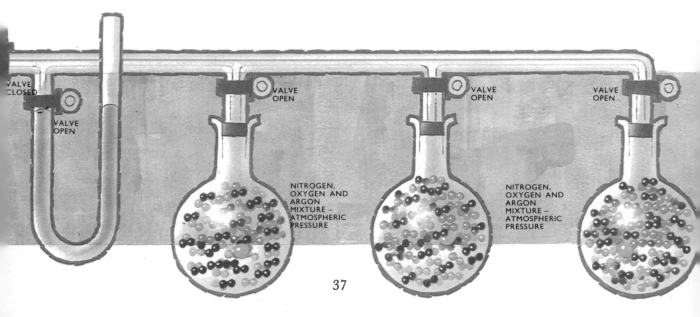

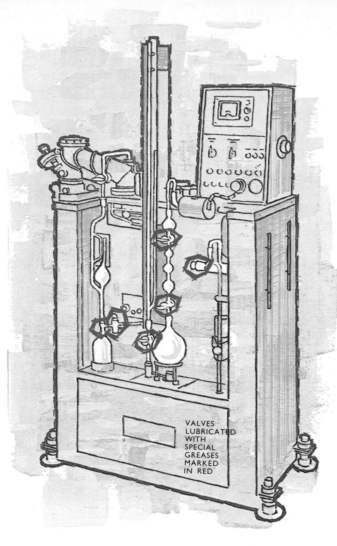

*This apparatus for measuring the gases dissolved in metals is run at a very low pressure. Special greases with negligible vapour pressures have to be used on the valves.*

respectively nitrogen, oxygen and argon at 177·9 cm, 48·0 cm, and 2·1 cm of mercury pressure respectively, are allowed to mix. Once the taps sealing the individual flasks are opened, molecules of all gases quickly diffuse into all three flasks, so the partial pressure of each gas will be one third of the pressure exerted by the separate gases in their original flasks. The partial pressure of the nitrogen is $\frac{1}{3} \times$ 177·9

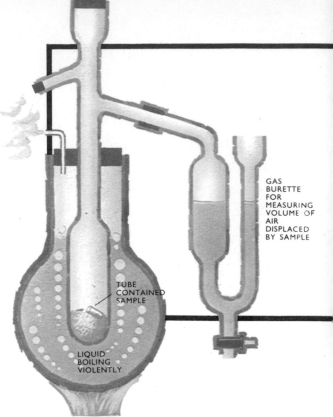

GAS BURETTE FOR MEASURING VOLUME OF AIR DISPLACED BY SAMPLE

TUBE CONTAINED SAMPLE

LIQUID BOILING VIOLENTLY

cm of mercury (cm Hg) = 59·3 cm Hg while that of oxygen is $\frac{1}{3} \times 48\cdot0 = 16\cdot0$ cm Hg and of argon is $\frac{1}{3} \times 2\cdot1 = 0\cdot7$ cm Hg. Adding together these three partial pressures gives the total pressure of the mixture = 59·3 + 16·0 + 0·7 = 76·0 cm Hg.

It is generally more convenient to collect insoluble gases over water, but the samples rapidly become contaminated with water vapour. In many instances it does not matter if there is water in the gas. However, the presence of water vapour will upset a measurement of gas set free in an experiment. This can be one of the largest sources of error in the Victor Meyer determination of vapour density and molecular weight of a volatile liquid.

In carrying out this experiment, the air displaced by the vaporized liquid is collected over water, so the air is

In a Victor Meyer determination of vapour density a sample displaced 63·70 cc of air, which was collected over water. Atmospheric pressure was 76·59 cm Hg. and the temperature 17°C. Before the vapour density and molecular weight of the sample can be found, the volume of (dry) air displaced must be reduced to S.T.P (0°C, 76·00 cm Hg).

(1) From tables the vapour pressure of water at 17°C = 1·45 cm Hg.

Pressure of dry air = total pressure — pressure of water vapour
= 76·59 — 1·45 = 75·14 cm Hg.

(2) To find volume of air at S.T.P.

$P_1$ = 75·14 cm Hg.   $T_1$ = 273°A + 17°C = 290°A.   $V_1$ = 63·70 cc
$P_2$ = 76·00 cm Hg.   $T_2$ = 273°A                      $V_2$ = ?

In the gas equation –

$$\frac{P_1 V_1}{T_1} = \frac{P_2 V_2}{T_2}$$

$$\frac{75·14 \times 63·70}{290} = \frac{76·00 \times V_2}{273}$$

Therefore   $V_2 = \frac{75·14 \times 63·70}{290} \times \frac{273}{76·00} = 59·3$ cc.

Thus volume of dry air at S.T.P. displaced by sample = 59·3cc

saturated with water vapour. The liquid level in the collecting vessel is then adjusted so that the air is at atmospheric pressure. The volume of gas and its temperature are noted. The vapour pressure of water at that temperature is found from tables and this is deducted from the atmospheric pressure (read on an accurate barometer). The total pressure in the container is the pressure of the dry air plus the pressure of the water vapour. Normally the volume of the gas is adjusted to the space it would occupy at standard temperature and pressure (o. C and 76·0 cm Hg pressure). This last calculation makes use of the *gas equation*.

When experiments are being carried out at very low pressures (i.e. under high vacuum), great care has to be taken in choosing the grease for lubricating valves in the apparatus. This is because some of the greases which would otherwise be suitable have a vapour pressure of the same order as that in the apparatus. Then, as the air is extracted by the vacuum pump, the pressure does not fall, because more grease evaporates. Therefore the grease chosen must have a very low vapour pressure.

*In a mixture of gases each gas exerts the same pressure as it would produce if it alone filled the space. Thus the nitrogen in the air exerts 78% (59·3 cm Hg) of the total pressure while the oxygen exerts only 21% (16·0 cm Hg).*

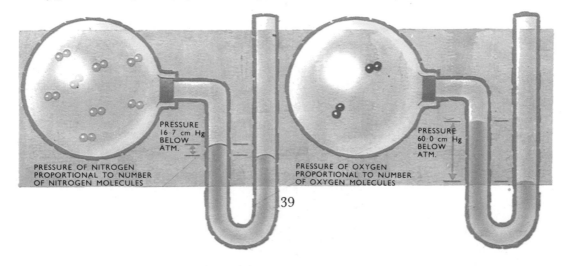

PRESSURE 16·7 cm Hg BELOW ATM.

PRESSURE OF NITROGEN PROPORTIONAL TO NUMBER OF NITROGEN MOLECULES

PRESSURE 60·0 cm Hg BELOW ATM.

PRESSURE OF OXYGEN PROPORTIONAL TO NUMBER OF OXYGEN MOLECULES

# CHAPTER FOURTEEN

# Phase Diagrams and Distillation

QUITE often the chemist has to separate two liquids that have been mixed together. If, like oil and water, they remain in separate globules and do not mingle thoroughly, then the answer is simple. Leave the mixture of liquids to stand and it separates out into layers. One layer can be poured off leaving the other behind.

But two liquids like ethyl alcohol and water do not remain as separate phases when they are mixed. They dissolve in one another forming a solution in which no globules of alcohol are suspended. No matter how long this solution is left to stand, it will never separate out but will always remain uniform throughout as a *single phase*. To separate the water from the ethyl alcohol, a different technique is needed.

For many liquid mixtures, distillation is the answer and almost complete separation can be obtained. But for some liquid mixtures this is quite impossible. A close study of the phase diagrams of these mixtures reveals why.

A phase diagram is a type of graph. Some of these are extremely complex, but the diagrams dealing with the distillation of a mixture of two liquids are relatively simple. Temperature is usually plotted along the vertical axis and the composition along the hori-

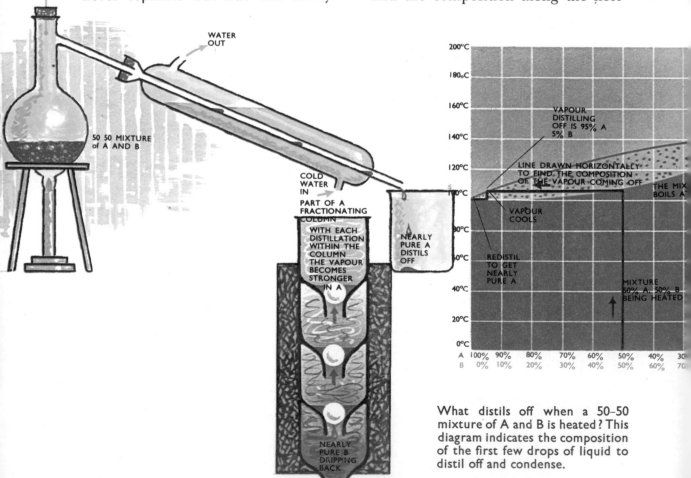

WATER OUT

50 50 MIXTURE of A and B

COLD WATER IN

PART OF A FRACTIONATING COLUMN

WITH EACH DISTILLATION WITHIN THE COLUMN THE VAPOUR BECOMES STRONGER IN A

NEARLY PURE A DISTILS OFF

NEARLY PURE B DRIPPING BACK

200°C
180°C
160°C
140°C
120°C
100°C
80°C
60°C
40°C
20°C
0°C

VAPOUR DISTILLING OFF IS 95% A 5% B

LINE DRAWN HORIZONTALLY TO FIND THE COMPOSITION OF THE VAPOUR COMING OFF

THE MIX BOILS A

VAPOUR COOLS

REDISTIL TO GET NEARLY PURE A

MIXTURE 50% A 50% B BEING HEATED

A  100%  90%  80%  70%  60%  50%  40%  30
B  0%  10%  20%  30%  40%  50%  60%  70

What distils off when a 50–50 mixture of A and B is heated? This diagram indicates the composition of the first few drops of liquid to distil off and condense.

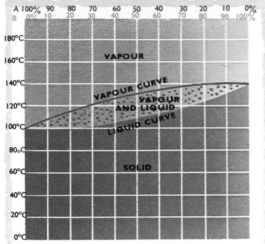

A phase diagram. Pure liquid A boils at 100°C and pure B boils at 140°C. The boiling points of mixtures of A and B are shown by the lower curve. The composition of the vapour boiling off is shown by the upper curve.

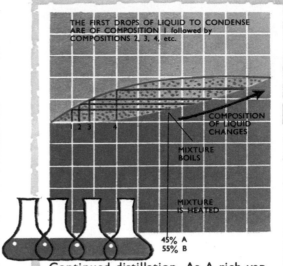

Continued distillation. As A-rich vapour comes off, the composition of the liquid left behind gradually changes. Consequently the composition of the distillate changes too.

zontal axis of the graph.

Zero on the horizontal axis represents one pure substance, i.e. the composition is 100% of one component and none of the other. The composition a little to the right of it will be 99% of that component and 1% of the other. The point at the far end of the line represents a composition of 100% of the other component. Half way along the line the composition is 50–50. Every possible composition is represented on this axis.

Two lines make up the graph, one representing the composition of the liquid being boiled and the upper line shows the composition of the vapour coming off.

If the liquids have different boiling points and the graph is made up of a single loop with the liquid and vapour lines which form the loop joining at each side of the graph, then the two liquids can be separated by distillation. But if the graph is of any other shape, then distillation will not separate them.

Why does only the one shape of graph give complete separation and the other not?

The two liquids to be separated must have different boiling points. Say A has a lower boiling point than B. When the liquid 50% A and 50% B is heated, the temperature rises until the boiling point of the mixture is reached. The lower curve represents the boiling liquid. The liquid boils and a vapour comes off, but the vapour is much richer in A. How rich? Draw a vertical line up from composition 50% A 50% B until the line reaches the lower curve. This is the boiling liquid. Extend the line from this point horizontally across until it cuts the upper curve. The point where it cuts represents the composition of the vapour being distilled off.

But the vapour is taking away more A, and as this happens the liquid left behind becomes increasingly more concentrated in B. As more vapour distils off the composition gradually changes, becoming more and more

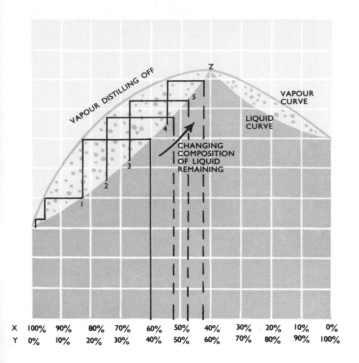

| X | 100% | 90% | 80% | 70% | 60% | 50% | 40% | 30% | 20% | 10% | 0% |
|---|---|---|---|---|---|---|---|---|---|---|---|
| Y | 0% | 10% | 20% | 30% | 40% | 50% | 60% | 70% | 80% | 90% | 100% |

*These two liquids cannot be completely separated by distillation. The starting liquid is 60% X, 40% Y. As vapour distils off, the liquid remaining behind becomes increasingly more concentrated in Y. When vapours 1, 2, 3 and 4 are redistilled several times pure X results. But when enough vapour has boiled off point Z is reached and the liquid of composition 40% X, 60% Y boils to give a vapour of the same composition. No further progress can be made.*

concentrated in B and weaker in A.

If small amounts of the vapour are collected and condensed and redistilled, the vapour becomes still more concentrated in A and the liquid left behind again grows stronger in B. To obtain completely pure A and completely pure B, this must be done over and over again.

No one wants the tedious task of condensing small fractions of vapour and redistilling again and again. The sensible thing is to use a fractionating column and let it do the job. The column is placed above the vessel in which the liquid mixture is being heated. Some of the vapour coming off condenses in the first section of the column. More vapour bubbles through, giving up some of its latent heat so that a vapour richer in A can

*These two liquids cannot be completely separated by distillation. Attempts are being made to separate a mixture which is 90% M and 10% L. As vapour distils off, the liquid remaining becomes increasingly more concentrated in M. But when the vapours 1, 2, and 3 are redistilled several times a liquid composition Z (50% L, 50% M) is obtained. The vapour coming off has the same composition as the boiling liquid, but pure M remains behind and will finally be distilled off pure (once all the 50–50 mixture is removed).*

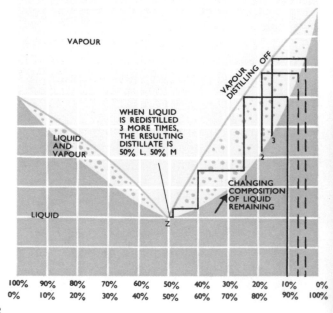

| L | 100% | 90% | 80% | 70% | 60% | 50% | 40% | 30% | 20% | 10% | 0% |
|---|---|---|---|---|---|---|---|---|---|---|---|
| M | 0% | 10% | 20% | 30% | 40% | 50% | 60% | 70% | 80% | 90% | 100% |

distil off to be condensed in the section above where the process is repeated. The liquid richer in B drips down the column. After a while the liquid dripping back is almost entirely B, while that emerging from the top of the column is nearly pure A.

The two other types of phase diagrams each consist of two loops which meet at a single point. In one type the loops arch upwards – like a cat with its back arched. The other type arches downwards – U-shaped. The point on the graph where the two loops meet represents a constant boiling mixture because at this point the vapour and liquid compositions are equal. In these cases fractional distillation will yield only a partial separation – i.e. the component in which the mixture is richer than the constant-boiling mixture will be obtained, either before the constant-boiling point is reached or after it, depending on whether the mixture has a maximum or minimum boiling point.

The phase diagrams show exactly why this happens. Just as before, it is best to pick a liquid of any composition and draw a line vertically upwards till it reaches the lower curve. Extend the line horizontally to find the composition of the vapour coming off. Repeat to find out what happens when the vapour is redistilled and take into consideration what is happening to the liquid left behind.

# CHAPTER FIFTEEN

# Steam Distillation

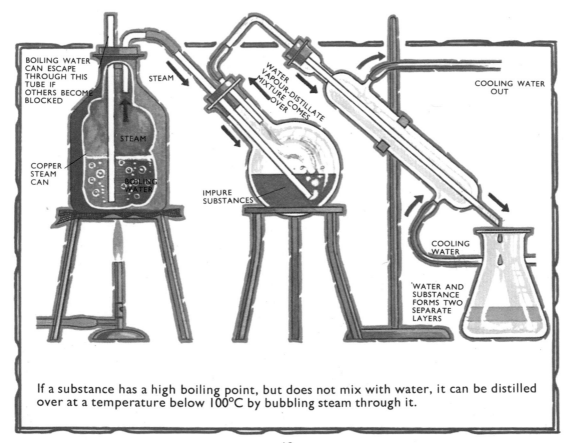

If a substance has a high boiling point, but does not mix with water, it can be distilled over at a temperature below 100°C by bubbling steam through it.

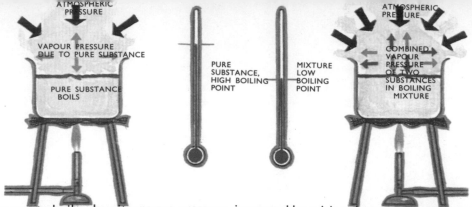

Pure water boils when its vapour pressure, increased by raising the temperature, equals atmospheric pressure. When chlorobenzene is added, the vapour pressure of the chlorobenzene is added to the vapour pressure of the water. The total vapour pressure is then increased with a rise in temperature and the mixture boils at a lower temperature than the pure water.

## How much chlorobenzene comes over with the water?

This depends on the partial pressure (p.p.) at the boiling point and the molecular weights (m.w.)

$$\frac{\text{mass of chlorobenzene}}{\text{mass of water}} =$$

$$\frac{\text{p.p. chlorobenzene}}{\text{p.p. water}} \times \frac{\text{m.w. chlorobenzene}}{\text{m.w. water}}$$

When the calculation is carried out (for an external pressure of 740 mm. of mercury) it is found that 71% of the distillate, by weight, should be chlorobenzene. This figure is verified in practice, so the steam distillation process is remarkably effective in bringing over the chlorobenzene at a temperature much lower than its boiling point.

ORGANIC chemicals with very high boiling points can often be purified by *steam distillation*.

Organic substances are rarely made pure in one single process. Usually the first preparation results in a mixture containing a host of unwanted substances which have to be removed at a later stage.

Distillation often provides the answer. But ordinary distillation has certain drawbacks. Crude chlorobenzene, $(C_6H_5Cl)$, with its many tarry impurities, presents this problem. Its boiling point is high ($132°C$), and therefore it must be heated strongly for distillation to begin. Some of the impurities start to char when it is strongly heated. Instead of boiling and bubbling gently, the contents start erupting and bumping and the far-too-hot flask could be cracked by a particularly violent bump.

Instead of heating the distillation flask with a Bunsen burner, the flask can be successfully heated by bubbling steam through its contents. The steam keeps the mixture well stirred and at a temperature of around $90°C$, a watery mixture of chlorobenzene distills off, leaving the impurities behind. The chlorobenzene is insoluble in water and the two quickly separate out into two easily separated layers

The crux of the matter is the insolubility of the chlorobenzene in water. Steam distillation will only work for substances that are virtually insoluble in water. For when two substances are immiscible in one another they are capable of quite independent behaviour.

Water and chlorobenzene are immiscible. Water on its own, when it is heated, evaporates more and more until at $100°C$ the pressure of its vapour has risen to that of its surroundings, and the water boils. Chlorobenzene on its own behaves similarly, but boils at the higher temperature of $132°C$. At a particular temperature, both pure liquids exert their own particular *vapour pressures*.

Mixing chlorobenzene with water will not alter these boiling points, for the two substances behave independently. At a particular temperature, the vapour pressure of the mixture can be calculated by adding the vapour pressure of the water to that of the chlorobenzene. So the mixture being heated more quickly arrives at the pressure of its surroundings than would either pure chlorobenzene or pure water. And the boiling point of the mixture is therefore lower than that of pure chlorobenzene or pure water. Steamy chlorobenzene is driven over into the condenser.

As the total vapour pressure in the distillation flask does not depend on the amount of steam or chlorobenzene present, the chlorobenzene will continue to distill off at the same temperature as long as there is any of it present.

# CHAPTER SIXTEEN

# Fractional Distillation

THE simplest form of distillation apparatus for use in the laboratory consists of a distillation flask, water-cooled condenser and receiver. But even in the laboratory such an arrangement has limitations, the main disadvantage being its inability to separate two liquids whose boiling points are fairly close together.

Although the boiling point of a liquid (A) may be 126° C., some evaporation will occur as its temperature is raised towards boiling point. If another liquid (B) which boils at 98°C. is mixed with A, rather more of liquid A than before is transferred from the distillation flask along with the vapours of boiling liquid B. Some

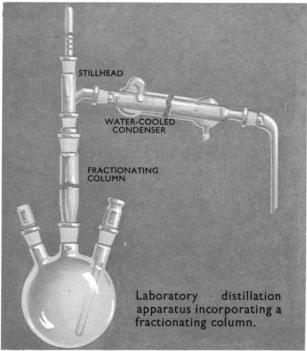

Simple laboratory distillation apparatus.

THERMOMETER

STILLHEAD

WATER-COOLED CONDENSER

ROUND BOTTOM FLASK

STILLHEAD

WATER-COOLED CONDENSER

FRACTIONATING COLUMN

Laboratory distillation apparatus incorporating a fractionating column.

of liquid A has been vaporized below its boiling point, but an even larger quantity of it is carried over into the condenser as fine liquid droplets in the form of a mist. These droplets of liquid A are swept out of the flask with the vapours of boiling liquid B. This effect can be reduced by not heating the flask too vigorously.

Thus even with the simple apparatus some separation of the liquid mixture into its two components is achieved. Samples collected in the receiver at the beginning of the separation will be found to be richer in liquid B, the *more volatile* component, than was the original mixture. (Since liquid B has the lower boiling point of the two components, it evaporates more readily, so it is said to be more volatile.) For a while the temperature of the vapour leaving the distillation flask will remain at about 98°C., and the distillate will continue to be rich in liquid B. However, when most of B has been distilled, the temperature of the vapour will rise rapidly to around 126°C. and the distillate will then be richer in liquid A, but there will still be some B as impurity.

Much more complete separation of the components of a liquid mixture can be obtained by inserting a *fractionating column* between the flask and the condenser. In this unit the separation of the more volatile from the less volatile component started in the flask is continued. Whereas in the simple apparatus a large proportion of the vapour flows directly into the condenser, some of the less volatile component condenses on the walls of the fractionating column and runs back into the flask.

The vapour leaving the flask is already richer in the more volatile substance than was the original liquid.

However, the degree of separation is improved still further as the vapour passes up the fractionating column. As the vapour rises upwards it is met by a flow of liquid coming down the column. This liquid is richer in the less volatile component.

Since heat is supplied to the foot of the column to evaporate the liquid, and heat is removed from the top of the column in condensing the vapour, it follows that there is a gradual reduction in temperature experienced by the vapour as it rises upwards. Thus there is an even greater tendency for the less volatile component to condense as it approaches the top of the column. The presence of the liquid flowing downwards encourages the less volatile component in the vapour to condense, while the up-flow of the vapour rich in the more volatile component tends to re-evaporate any of this component which has condensed.

In order that this process of condensation and re-evaporation may proceed efficiently it is essential that the vapour and liquid phases are brought into contact with one another as they flow up and down the column. To achieve good contacting, the liquid phase must be spread over as large an area as possible since such liquid/vapour exchanges only take place at the surface of the liquid.

Various methods are used, both in the laboratory and on a commercial scale, to spread the descending liquid film over as large an area as possible. In some laboratory columns the glass surfaces have been specially shaped with wrinkles and folds to increase the surface area. Another technique which is used industrially as well as in the laboratory is to pack the column with small hollow cylinders of porous pottery or small spirals of metal foil.

# CHAPTER SEVENTEEN

# Solubility of Gases

BOTH ammonia and hydrogen chloride are very soluble in water. In fact at 15°C water will absorb 800 times its own volume of ammonia at normal atmospheric pressure. Their high solubility may be demonstrated in a quite spectacular way by the *Fountain Experiment*, so called because a fountain of water droplets rushes into the flask which originally contained the gas.

The arrangement of the apparatus is shown in the diagram.

Carbon dioxide gives the fizz to fizzy drinks. It is forced into the lemonade under pressure and then the bottle top is screwed on tightly so that the gas cannot escape. The carbon dioxide has obviously dissolved in the lemonade as there are few bubbles to be seen in the bottle. But immediately the stopper is removed and the pressure is released, the lemonade starts fizzing and the bottle is full of rising bubbles. Most of the carbon dioxide can no longer remain in solution and so forms gas bubbles which rush up to the surface and escape into the atmosphere.

More carbon dioxide dissolves in lemonade when it is forced in *under pressure* than dissolves when the pressure is lower. This is a general rule for all gases dissolving in liquids. Solubility increases with increase of gas pressure.

But exactly how does gas pressure affect the solubility? At 0°C and

*Once the water has entered the flask containing ammonia (left) the flow of water continues without further assistance. As the ammonia dissolves, the pressure of the gas in the flask drops. The greater pressure of the atmosphere makes more water rush into the flask. A similar effect is observed with a flask full of steam (right), but here the pressure falls as the steam cools.*

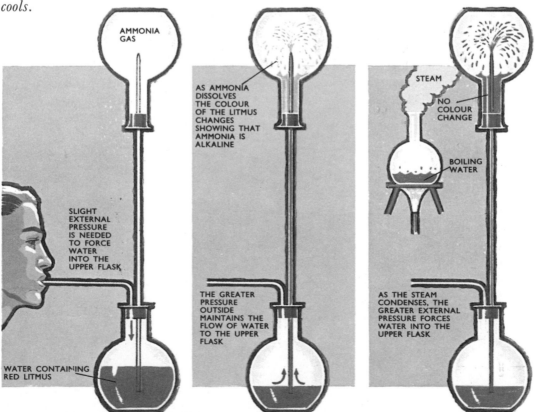

AMMONIA GAS

AS AMMONIA DISSOLVES THE COLOUR OF THE LITMUS CHANGES SHOWING THAT AMMONIA IS ALKALINE

STEAM

NO COLOUR CHANGE

BOILING WATER

SLIGHT EXTERNAL PRESSURE IS NEEDED TO FORCE WATER INTO THE UPPER FLASK

THE GREATER PRESSURE OUTSIDE MAINTAINS THE FLOW OF WATER TO THE UPPER FLASK

AS THE STEAM CONDENSES, THE GREATER EXTERNAL PRESSURE FORCES WATER INTO THE UPPER FLASK

WATER CONTAINING RED LITMUS

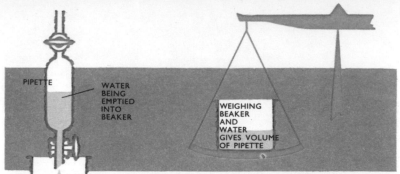

## Apparatus for finding the solubility of a gas in a liquid

*The volume of the pipette is found by finding the mass of water to fill it. If the mass is 120 gram, then the volume is approximately 120 cc.*

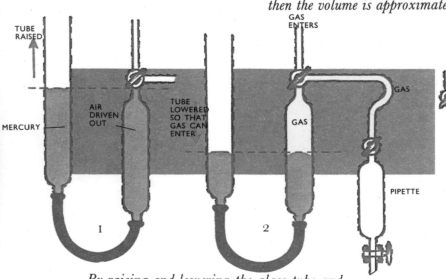

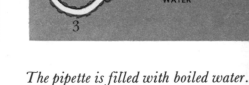

*The pipette is filled with boiled water.*

*By raising and lowering the glass tube and adjusting the taps, the burette and connecting tube are filled with gas.*

*Some of the boiled water is quickly run out of the pipette and weighed so that the volume remaining can be found. The mercury is levelled and the burette reading is noted. 5. The water is shaken with gas and left in a thermostatically controlled bath to ensure total saturation. 6. The rise in mercury level is the volume of gas that has dissolved at the pressure of the room.*

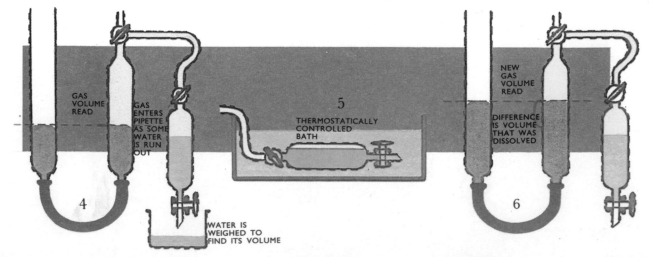

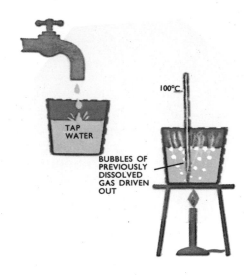

*Tap water contains dissolved gases. When the water nears boiling point, bubbles are seen rising. The gas is driven out as the temperature rises.*

atmospheric pressure, 0·00188 grams of hydrogen will dissolve in 1 litre of gas-free water. When the gas pressure is doubled, the mass of hydrogen dissolved is also doubled. 0·00376 grams then dissolve. Trebling the gas pressure also trebles the mass of gas going into solution. In other words, *mass of gas dissolving in a given volume of liquid at a given temperature is directly proportional to the gas pressure.* This is known as *Henry's Law.*

Carbon monoxide, nitrogen, oxygen and hydrogen all obey this law very well. When the gas pressure is doubled, the solubility is also doubled. Sulphur dioxide, ammonia and hydrogen chloride gas do not obey the Law however. These are gases with high solubilities in water and there is no general rule describing their behaviour. Henry's Law only applies to gases which are relatively insoluble in the particular solvent under consideration.

When hydrogen chloride dissolves

in water it forms hydrochloric acid. Ammonia gas forms ammonium hydroxide and sulphur dioxide dissolves to form sulphurous acid. All are quite soluble and have undergone a chemical reaction. It is therefore reasonable to assume that when a gas disobeys Henry's Law the gas reacts chemically with the solvent.

Carbon dioxide lies between these two types. It follows Henry's Law but not very closely. A little of the gas reacts with water forming carbonic acid and the rest goes into solution and obeys Henry's Law.

Temperature also affects gas solubility. There are no gas bubbles to be seen in a glass of water. But when the same sample of water is heated towards its boiling point bubbles begin

## Finding the solubility of a gas in a liquid

It is quite easy to find the *volume* of gas dissolving under certain conditions but difficult to find the dissolving mass directly. Consequently the volume is found by experiment and the mass is calculated from it.

For example, the results of an experiment could show that 21 cc of hydrogen at 0°C and atmospheric pressure (760 mm of mercury) dissolve in 1000 cc of boiled water. No matter what the gas, a molecular weight of it expressed in grams occupies 22,400 cc at 0°C and 760 mm pressure. So under these conditions, 2 grams of hydrogen occupies 22,400 cc. A volume of 21 cc, then has a mass of

$$\frac{2 \times 21}{22,400} = 0\cdot00188 \text{ gram}$$

The apparatus for finding gas solubilities consists of an open-ended tube of thick glass which can be moved up and down. The lower end is connected by thick walled rubber tubing to another glass tube (burette), this one graduated with volume measurements. At the top of the burette is a 3-way tap which can connect the system to the gas supply or to a pipette. The idea is to put the liquid in the pipette and find out what volume of gas it absorbs.

49

to form and rise up to the surface. Although a certain amount of air can dissolve in water at room temperature it is driven out as the temperature rises. The air can be completely driven out by boiling the water.

If a corked bottle of fizzy drink is left in the sun, bubbles of carbon dioxide start to come out of solution. The pressure of gas above the drink starts to build up until the cork can no longer hold in place and pops out of the bottle.

Gas solubility, then, decreases with rise in temperature. Usually all the dissolved gas can be driven out of a liquid by boiling it. This is the general behaviour pattern, but no definite rule is followed. The decrease in solubility with temperature is not a steady one. If the solubility of a gas is known at a certain temperature and pressure, it is impossible to calculate the solubility when the temperature is altered. The only way to find the new solubility is to find it by experiment.

# CHAPTER EIGHTEEN

# Purification of Gases

SINCE several of the gases made in the laboratory are frequently collected over water, it is hardly surprising that the products are contaminated with water vapour. Usually the presence of moisture in a sample of gas does not affect its properties, nor are its reactions with other substances upset. There are occasions, however, when it is necessary for the gas to be dried and this can be achieved by passing it over substances which readily absorb water.

Great care is taken to remove the water because the smallest trace

might, in an otherwise pure substance, have profound effects on its chemical properties. Chlorine gas, for example, when absolutely pure and dry, is not particularly reactive, but when the slightest trace of moisture is present it becomes one of the most reactive gases known.

To remove moisture, the chemist has at his disposal a number of drying agents (*desiccants*).

Concentrated sulphuric acid, phosphorus pentoxide, calcium oxide (quicklime) and anhydrous calcium chloride are among the compounds which can be used for this purpose. But, since several of them are quite reactive substances, great care must be exercised in choosing the best one for drying a particular gas. Clearly, the drying agent should not react with the gas. Thus an acidic drying agent like concentrated sulphuric acid must not be used for drying ammonia gas which is strongly basic. In fact ammonia reacts violently with concentrated sulphuric acid to yield ammonium sulphate:

## Preparation of Dry Nitrogen

*After making the gas by warming a solution of ammonium chloride and sodium nitrate, it is dried by passing it through a U-Tube containing calcium chloride. The nitrogen is collected over mercury in a special porcelain dish.*

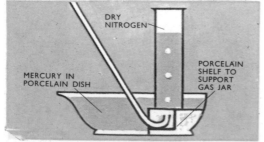

DRY NITROGEN

MERCURY IN PORCELAIN DISH

PORCELAIN SHELF TO SUPPORT GAS JAR

50

$$2NH_3 + H_2SO_4 = (NH_4)_2SO_4$$

ammonia    sulphuric    ammonium
           acid         sulphate

Calcium oxide is found to be the most satisfactory substance for drying ammonia, and drying is certainly necessary as ammonia is very soluble in water.

For similar reasons calcium oxide (a basic oxide) is not suitable for drying hydrogen chloride gas. Neither can phosphorus pentoxide be used, as the gas is slowly absorbed with the formation of phosphorus oxychloride:

$$2P_2O_5 + 3HCl$$

phosphorus    hydrogen
pentoxide     chloride

$$= POCl_3 + 3HPO_3$$

phosphorus    metaphosphoric
oxychloride   acid

Concentrated sulphuric acid, however, does not react with the gas and is

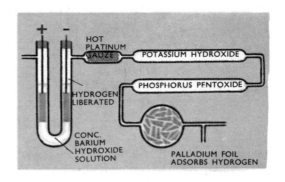

*Diagram of apparatus in which very pure hydrogen is prepared. The gas which is obtained by the electrolysis of barium hydroxide solution contains traces of oxygen, carbon dioxide as well as water vapour. First oxygen is removed by passing the gas over hot platinum gauze, then the carbon dioxide combines with the potassium hydroxide. Moisture is absorbed by the phosphorus pentoxide crystals, and finally the pure hydrogen is adsorbed on to the palladium foil.*

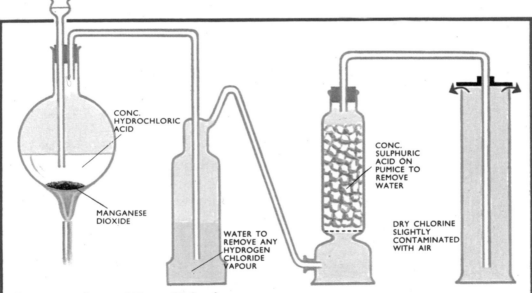

## Preparation of Dry Chlorine

Hydrogen chloride vapour is set free when chlorine is prepared by the action of concentrated hydrochloric acid on manganese dioxide. This acid vapour may be removed by bubbling the gas through water before it is dried by passing it up a tower containing lumps of pumice soaked in concentrated sulphuric acid. As chlorine attacks mercury it is collected by upward displacement of air.

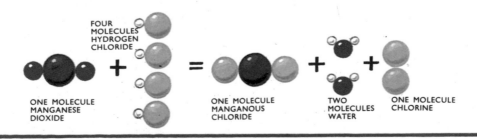

most frequently used when moisture-free samples are required.

Care must also be taken if a sample of dry hydrogen sulphide is required, since colloidal sulphur is formed when the gas is passed through concentrated sulphuric acid:

$$H_2S + H_2SO_4 = S + SO_2 + 2H_2O$$
hydrogen sulphuric sulphur sulphur water
sulphide acid dioxide

Quite good drying can be achieved by passing the gas over calcium chloride, but the best results are obtained by liquefying the gas and then redistilling it. (Hydrogen sulphide condenses to yield a colourless liquid boiling at $-60 \cdot 7°C$).

Solid drying agents are usually packed in towers or U-tubes and these are inserted between the vessel in which the gas is actually made and the collection apparatus. If concentrated sulphuric acid is used it may be placed in a wash bottle, so that the gas is dried as each bubble rises through the acid. However, such an arrangement tends to create acid droplets which are carried along with the dry gas. A more satisfactory alternative is to soak lumps of pumice (porous rock of volcanic origin) in the concentrated acid and to pack the pieces in a drying tower.

Once a gas has been dried by one of the methods suggested above, it would be foolish to collect samples over water. One alternative is to collect the gas over mercury, provided that there is no reaction between the two – chlorine, for example, attacks mercury and mercuric chloride is formed.

Not only is mercury expensive, it is also dense, so it is not practicable to replace the water in an ordinary pneumatic trough with mercury. Troughs made of porcelain have been designed with this problem in mind,

and are specially shaped so that a shelf to support the gas jar is an integral part of the trough. Alternatively, if contamination with small quantities of air is permissible, the gas may be collected by upward or downward displacement of air depending upon the relative densities of air and the gas.

Water is, perhaps, the contaminant to be found most frequently in the gases prepared in the laboratory and will invariably be present in a sample if there is water in the reaction vessel. Water may be there as the solvent for the sulphuric acid in the preparation of hydrogen, or may be a by-product of the reaction as in the preparation of ammonia.

Contamination of a sample by substances other than water is in many instances a direct consequence of using reactants which themselves contain impurities. Clearly, one way of overcoming this problem is to use only those reactants which are available in a high state of purity. This may even mean abandoning the usual laboratory method of preparation for a more sophisticated one if this yields a product of better quality.

Thus hydrogen is often obtained by the action of a dilute acid on zinc or magnesium, but the best method of obtaining *very pure hydrogen* is to electro-

**Agents for Drying Common Gases**

| Gas | Drying Agent |
| --- | --- |
| Oxygen | phosphorus pentoxide |
| Hydrogen | calcium chloride |
| Nitrous oxide | conc. sulphuric acid |
| Nitrogen | calcium chloride |
| Ammonia | calcium oxide |
| Carbon dioxide | any |
| Carbon monoxide | phosphorus pentoxide |
| Chlorine | conc. sulphuric acid |
| Hydrogen chloride | conc. sulphuric acid |
| Hydrogen sulphide | calcium chloride |
| Sulphur dioxide | any |

lyse a solution of barium hydroxide. After traces of oxygen and carbon dioxide have been removed and the gas dried, hydrogen is adsorbed on to pieces of palladium foil from which it can be regenerated by heating.

Another common source of contamination is acid spray or acid vapour. This may be reduced, though not altogether eliminated, by mixing the reactants in such a way that the reaction does not proceed too vigorously. The problem is most serious in preparations using hydrochloric acid, since the heat of reaction alone may be sufficient to vapourize the acid.

Unless the gas itself is soluble, the acid may be removed from it by bubbling the gas through water. This is particularly important in the preparation of chlorine gas by the action of manganese dioxide on concentrated hydrochloric acid. If a gas is collected over water (or brine in the case of chlorine) it will probably be free from acid, since the gas bubbles will have passed through the water in the pneumatic trough. However, if the gas were required dry, this source of contamination could be easily overlooked, since a different method of collection would be used.

# CHAPTER NINETEEN

# Drying Agents

SOME drying agents merely take water into their surface structures – silica gel, for example. Others remove water as a result of a chemical reaction. For example, concentrated sulphuric acid will remove water of crystallization from copper sulphate crystals, turning it from the blue form to the white anhydrous form:

$$CuSO_4, 5H_2O \rightarrow CuSO_4 + 5H_2O$$
blue · · · · · · · · · · · white

In an even more powerful reaction, it drags water right out of the sugar molecule, leaving behind a black mass of carbon:

$$C_{12}H_{22}O_{11} \rightarrow 12C + 11H_2O$$
sucrose · · · carbon · · · water

Though it is obviously a good drying agent sulphuric acid must be used with care because of its properties as a powerful acid and oxidizing agent.

There are a number of solid desiccants that might be used in the laboratory. These are often anhydrous forms of crystals that take up water of crystallisation, although phosphorus pentoxide – a very efficient desiccant, is turned into a wet mass of phosphoric acid by the water it absorbs. A more commonly used one is anhydrous

*The solid to be dried is placed in a sealed dessicator. The atmosphere is kept dry by the dessicant, which may be one of a number of compounds, depending on the degree of dryness required.*

SPECIMEN TO BE DRIED

DRYING AGENT IN DISH

calcium chloride. To dry a gas the solid is placed in a drying tube and the gas is passed over it. To dry liquids (particularly organic compounds) the solid calcium chloride is dropped into the liquid and allowed to stand for a few hours. Then the liquid is passed through a coarse glass wool filter and the solid, which has taken up the water from the organic liquid, is separated out. Other solids used in organic chemistry are anhydrous magnesium sulphate and anhydrous sodium sulphate. These are slower in action than calcium chloride.

The most drastic way of drying a solid is to heat it to dryness, but this cannot always be done because the solid might decompose at high temperatures. A safer method is to dry the solid in a *desiccator*. This is a sealed vessel in which the damp solid is placed on a watch glass. The drying agent – sulphuric acid, calcium chloride, or phosphorus pentoxide is placed in the base of the desiccator. The water vapour in the atmosphere in the desiccator is quickly absorbed by the desiccant and as more comes off the damp solid this is removed, too.

The desiccator is also used as a cooling vessel. When a solid is dried by heating, it is essential that it cools in a dry atmosphere to prevent absorption of moisture from the atmosphere. This is ensured by allowing it to cool off in the dry atmosphere of the desiccator.

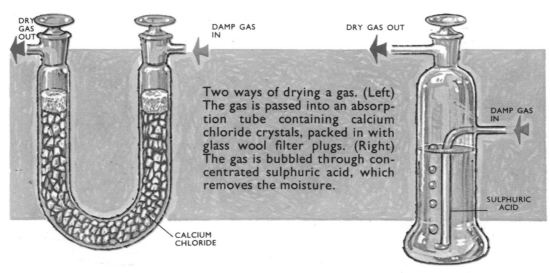

Two ways of drying a gas. (Left) The gas is passed into an absorption tube containing calcium chloride crystals, packed in with glass wool filter plugs. (Right) The gas is bubbled through concentrated sulphuric acid, which removes the moisture.

DRY GAS OUT

DAMP GAS IN

DRY GAS OUT

DAMP GAS IN

SULPHURIC ACID

CALCIUM CHLORIDE

# Qualitative Analysis

# CHAPTER TWENTY

# The Chemist at Work

BEFORE anyone can embark upon a career in chemistry a thorough knowledge of chemical reactions and of the chemical properties of substances must be gained. This provides a valuable background but a large number of chemists make comparatively little direct use of this general chemistry in their day-to-day work which is probably highly specialized.

According to the type of work they do chemists may be divided into two large groups – *analysts* and *research workers*.

Those who are engaged in chemical research – either making new compounds, finding better and possibly cheaper methods of manufacturing other substances for which there is already a demand, or investigating more fully the behaviour of substances, sometimes under extreme conditions of temperature or pressure – make little direct use of their general chemical knowledge. Instead of using ordinary text-books as a source of information, the specialist must refer to articles in scientific journals.

However, there are probably a larger number of chemists who are concerned in some way with *analysis*. There are many circumstances in which it is necessary to know which

*In order that analysis, particularly for trace elements, shall be as accurate as possible great care must be taken by the chemist to ensure that 'foreign' impurities are not introduced into a sample. Solutions must therefore be made up from pure water, such as is obtained from the* ion exchange resin column *shown.*

substances are present in a sample. It may be vital to know how much of some of these materials, particularly those which are only present in small amounts, there is in the sample.

By means of *inorganic qualitative analysis*, the elements or radicals present in a sample of an inorganic material may be found. This is achieved by carrying out a whole series of short experiments, usually called tests. The order of the tests has been carefully worked out so that the various components of the mixture are gradually removed from the solution. (The sample has first to be dissolved in water or acid.) The formation of a precipitate, or the evolution of a gas following the addition of a certain substance, indicates the pre-

sence of a particular metal or radical.

After the components of the sample have been identified, it may be desirable to know how much of the different substances is present. This branch of chemistry is known as *quantitative analysis*. The determinations may be made by removing the required metal or radical from a solution in the form of an insoluble compound. The solid removed from solution is usually filtered, dried and weighed; hence methods in which a precipitate are weighed are referred to as *gravimetric*. Once the amount of solid removed from solution is known, it is possible to calculate the proportion of the metal which was present in the original sample.

Certain types of estimation lend themselves to *volumetric analysis*. By this technique, the concentration of some substances already in solution, or solids which are soluble, may be found by the steady addition of known volumes of another solution with which they react. The composition of the other solution, generally known as a *standard solution*, must be known accurately. In addition there must be a means of finding out when all of the active constituent of the solution under examination has been used up. This is often done by means of an *indicator*. If the amount of alkali in solution is to be found, acid is added until the alkali has been neutralized, and litmus or a similar substance is used as the indicator. The colour of the solution will change from blue when it is alkaline to red as soon as there is a slight excess of acid.

The techniques outlined above refer to the detection and estimation of inorganic substances rather than organic ones.

Analysts are employed in a great variety of industries and in almost all instances their work will ultimately benefit the user or consumer of the end product of that particular industry. Some of them work for the producers to ensure that the articles which are sold are of the required standard, while other analysts are employed by various government

*Once a new method of making a substance has been devised, it is necessary to purify the product. Here a mixture of liquids is being separated by distillation.*

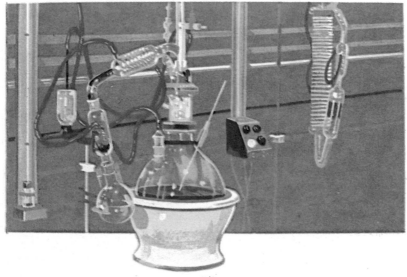

departments as a check on the manufacturer's claims regarding the composition of the product. They are more concerned, however, that the statutory regulations, particularly regarding foodstuffs, have been met.

Frequent regular chemical tests are carried out on the public water supply to ensure that it is fit to drink. Harmful bacteria are removed by chlorination, but if the amount of chlorine remaining in solution rises above a certain level, the water is unpleasant to drink. The concentration of chlorine is, therefore, watched carefully. In some areas it is possible for traces of toxic metals to become dissolved in the water. This applies particularly to very soft water which often tends to be acidic. It is equally important that these metals are looked for in all samples.

Analysis is carried out on the gas supply both to confirm that it has the heating capacity which the gas board claims and also that no hydrogen sulphide gas remains in the

purified product. As an important constituent of town gas is the odourless, poisonous gas carbon monoxide, steps are taken to ensure that the gas has an easily detected unpleasant odour.

Waste gases and waste liquids (including the treated effluent from sewage disposal works) must be analysed as a precaution against unpleasant and dangerous substances being set free in the atmosphere or discharged into rivers. A stricter control over the harmful gases and fine dust particles which are allowed into the atmosphere should go a long way towards reducing fog.

In factories where foodstuffs are processed routine quality checks have to be made at various stages. Cer-

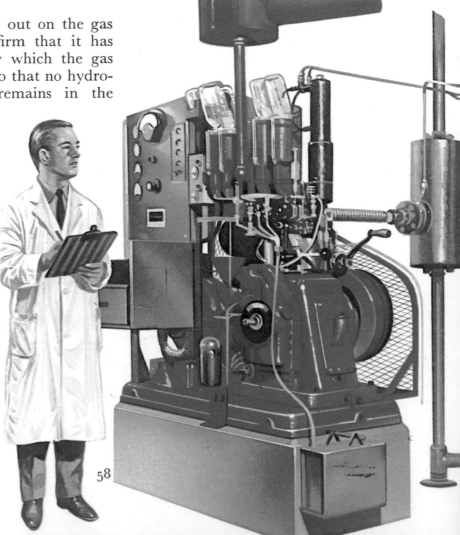

*An engine in which motor fuels are tested for anti-knock properties. Each sample's performance is compared with mixtures of normal heptane $(C_7H_{16})$ and iso-octane $(C_8H_{18})$.*

58

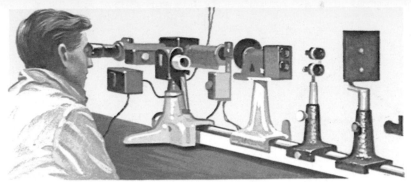

*A number of electrical and mechanical devices are used in the routine testing of products. Here a spectrophotometer is being used for quality control in a foodstuffs testing laboratory.*

tainly the various raw materials have to be analysed before they are accepted. The end product must also pass statutory tests. The analyst will also ensure that the product will not cause corrosion with packaging containers such as cans.

There are many other fields in which analysts work, but space prevents more than a brief reference to them. In the refining of metals tests are made to ensure that undesirable metals and non-metals are excluded, and to make certain that in alloys the small quantities of the additional metals are present in the correct proportions.

Analysts work in hospitals to assist the doctors in diagnosing diseases and tracing the recovery of the patients. Yet another field of work is in the forensic laboratories in which chemists and experts in other sciences (e.g. biology) play their part in crime detection.

In those instances where the same type of samples are being analysed regularly for the same constituents it is often possible to do much of the work using mechanical aids. A number of special automatic recording devices have been developed for taking and analysing samples at regular intervals.

# CHAPTER TWENTY-ONE

# Preliminary Analysis

BEFORE starting the main analysis of an inorganic substance, it is necessary to carry out a *preliminary analysis*. This only takes about 20 minutes. During this time many of the metallic radicals (e.g. copper) and acid radicals (e.g. chloride) can be detected. Their presence will be confirmed at a later stage.

Results for each stage of the analysis should be written down in columns under the headings of *test*, *observation* and *conclusion*, leaving nothing to memory.

Often the *appearance* of a substance can give a valuable clue to its composition. For example, many copper salts are blue; some are green. Hydrated chromic and ferrous salts are also green. Hydrated ferric salts and chromates are yellow and hydrated cobalt salts and permanganates in solution are crimson or purple.

Then, quite a lot can be learned by *heating* the sample quite strongly. A tiny hard glass test tube is used because it must be thrown away afterwards. Sodium chloride, lead

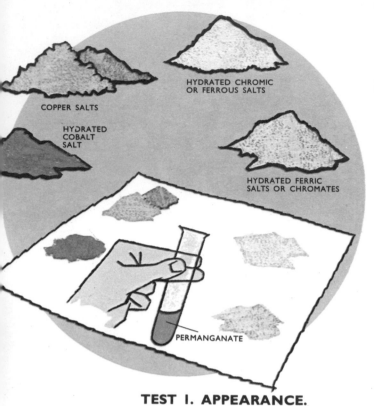

**TEST 1. APPEARANCE.**

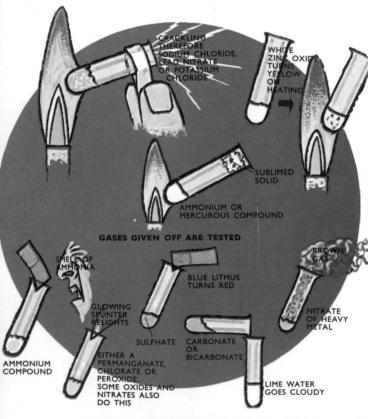

**TEST 2. STRONGLY HEAT SOME DRY SOLID.**

nitrate and potassium chloride make crackling noises when heated in this way. Some other compounds change colour. White zinc oxide turns yellow. Some ammonium and mercurous compounds *sublime*. This means that the solid vaporizes and forms a solid deposit on the cold upper parts of the tube.

From some compounds gases are given off. Ammonia can be detected by its *smell* and if it is given off, there must be an ammonium compound present. Pieces of moist red and blue *litmus* paper are held at the mouth of the tube. Ammonia gas turns the red litmus blue. Some sulphates give off the acidic gas, sulphur trioxide, which turns blue litmus red. The gas is next tested with a *glowing* wooden splinter. When oxygen is given off, the splinter relights itself. Permanganates, peroxides, sodium or potassium nitrate, or oxides of silver or mercury all give off oxygen when heated. If carbonates are present, then carbon dioxide is given off. This is detected by holding a test tube containing a little lime water below the neck of the heated tube. Carbon dioxide turns the lime water milky.

Some metallic ions can be detected by the *flame test*. A little of the solid sample is put on one watch glass and a few drops of concentrated hydrochloric acid on another. The end of a fine porcelain rod is dipped first into the acid and then into the sample. When it is held in a Bunsen flame sometimes the flame becomes coloured. The colour depends upon the metal present. Compounds of sodium give an intense yellow flame, strontium, a flicker of crimson, copper bluish green, calcium orange, barium apple green and potassium lilac. Because the lilac flame is difficult to see, the flame should next be viewed through blue glass. Then it becomes clearly visible as a crimson flame. The dirty part of the porcelain rod is broken off and thrown away, leaving the rest of the rod clean and ready for future use.

More metallic radicals are detected by the *borax bead test*. By heating a loop of clean platinum wire, dipping it in borax powder and holding it in a roaring flame, a colourless bead of borax is made in the loop. Touching the bead lightly against the solid sample collects just a little of it. The bead is re-heated in the outer part of a roaring Bunsen flame when it sometimes becomes coloured. Copper colours it light blue or green, chromium emerald green, cobalt deep blue and manganese purple. Nickel gives a permanent brown colour. The brown colour caused by iron turns yellow when the bead has cooled down. As with the flame test a mixture of these metals gives no useful result, for one colour can mask another.

Compounds of certain metals can be recognized by reduction to the metals themselves. This is done in the *charcoal block* test. Sodium carbonate is used to convert the unknown salt into the carbonate. Charcoal (a form of carbon) is the reducing agent used to rob the metal of its carbonate partner. A penknife is used to scoop a hole out of a block of charcoal and remove any debris from previous tests. A mixture of sample and anhydrous sodium carbonate is pressed into the hole. The airhole in the Bunsen is closed to make the flame luminous and the gas is turned down to make the flame only two inches high. (A taller flame can easily set fire to the analyst's hair). A blowpipe is used to direct the flame on to the sample. With practice it is quite easy to breathe through the nose and

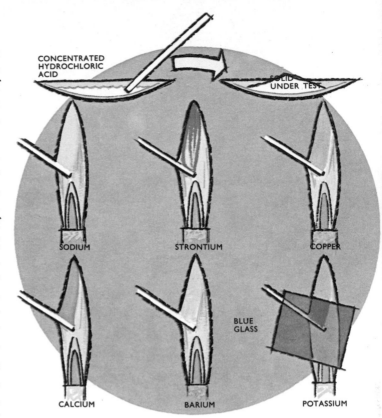

CONCENTRATED HYDROCHLORIC ACID

SOLID UNDER TEST

SODIUM    STRONTIUM    COPPER

BLUE GLASS

CALCIUM    BARIUM    POTASSIUM

**TEST 3. FLAME TEST.**

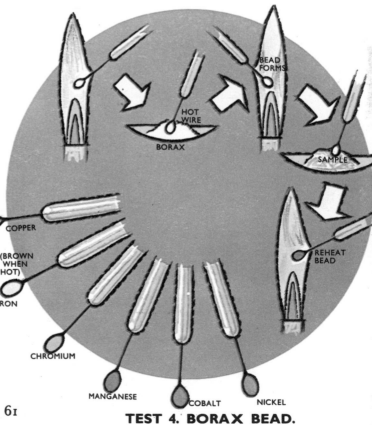

BEAD FORMS

HOT WIRE

BORAX

SAMPLE

REHEAT BEAD

COPPER

(BROWN WHEN HOT)

IRON

CHROMIUM

MANGANESE    COBALT    NICKEL

**TEST 4. BORAX BEAD.**

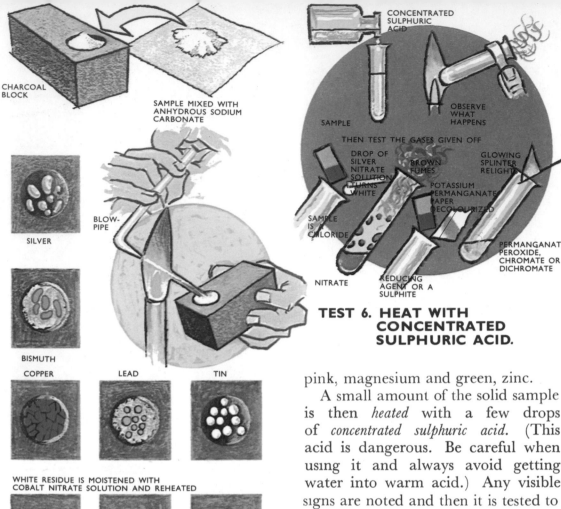

CHARCOAL BLOCK

SAMPLE MIXED WITH ANHYDROUS SODIUM CARBONATE

CONCENTRATED SULPHURIC ACID

SAMPLE

OBSERVE WHAT HAPPENS

THEN TEST THE GASES GIVEN OFF

DROP OF SILVER NITRATE SOLUTION TURNS WHITE

BROWN FUMES

GLOWING SPLINTER RELIGHTS

POTASSIUM PERMANGANATE PAPER DECOLOURIZED

SAMPLE IS A CHLORIDE

PERMANGANATE PEROXIDE, CHROMATE OR DICHROMATE

NITRATE

REDUCING AGENT OR A SULPHITE

BLOW-PIPE

SILVER

BISMUTH

COPPER

LEAD

TIN

WHITE RESIDUE IS MOISTENED WITH COBALT NITRATE SOLUTION AND REHEATED

ALUMINIUM        MAGNESIUM        ZINC

## TEST 5. CHARCOAL BLOCK.

blow steadily down the pipe. With lead, grey beads of the metal are left behind. When they are rubbed across a sheet of paper they leave a grey mark. Copper leaves red scales, tin hard white beads, silver soft shining particles and bismuth brittle pink blobs. If garlic smelling fumes are given off, arsenic is responsible. For zinc, the residue is yellow when hot and white when cold. If after heating, the residue is a white powder it should be moistened (not flooded) with a drop of pink cobalt nitrate solution and re-heated. If it turns blue it is aluminium,

## TEST 6. HEAT WITH CONCENTRATED SULPHURIC ACID.

pink, magnesium and green, zinc.

A small amount of the solid sample is then *heated* with a few drops of *concentrated sulphuric acid*. (This acid is dangerous. Be careful when using it and always avoid getting water into warm acid.) Any visible signs are noted and then it is tested to see if any gases are coming off, first with a lighted and then glowing splinter, finally with some moistened blue litmus paper. If steamy acidic fumes come off, they should be further tested with a drop of silver nitrate solution held on the end of a glass rod. A milkiness shows that a chloride is present. Harsh-smelling acidic fumes of sulphur dioxide remove the colour from a piece of filter paper that has been soaked in purple potassium permanganate solution. These could be caused by a reducing agent such as iron filings or a sulphite. A brownish gas with oily drops collecting on the sides of the tube indicates a nitrate.

The next acid test is with *dilute hydrochloric acid*. If there is no reaction in the cold, the test tube is gently heated. Any gases given off are smel-

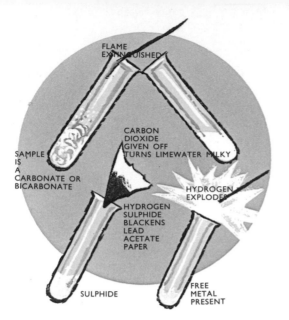

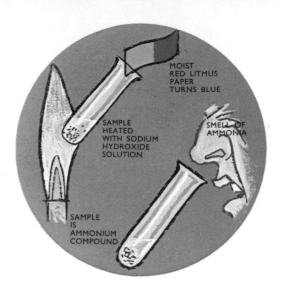

## TEST 7. DILUTE HYDROCHLORIC ACID.

## TEST 8. CAUSTIC SODA SOLUTION.

led, tested with a lighted splint and finally tested with lime water. Sulphides give off a smell of bad eggs. Carbonates and bicarbonates fizz as carbon dioxide gas is evolved. Free uncombined metals such as magnesium give off hydrogen. This explodes with a popping noise when tested with a lighted splinter.

All the tests performed so far only give an indication of what might be

present, not what definitely is there. But the next test with *caustic soda* solution is the only test for ammonium salts. It is most important that this last test should never be forgotten. Caustic soda solution is added and the test tube is gently warmed. If a smell of ammonia comes off and a piece of moist red litmus paper turns blue then there is definitely an ammonium compound present.

## THE NEGATIVE RADICALS

AFTER the preliminary tests the analyst begins a systematic series of tests to confirm his preliminary findings.

In the analysis, the sample is first put into solution (if it is solid) and the tests carried out on the solution. First, any *acid radicals* that have not already been detected in the preliminary tests are identified. Then the *metals* are detected by the systematic elimination of groups of metals by bringing their insoluble salts out of solution.

The presence of sulphide, sulphite, thiosulphate, nitrite, hypochlorite, carbonate and bicarbonate radicals

should already have been noted from the preliminary test with dilute hydrochloric acid. Likewise, the action of concentrated sulphuric acid ought to have indicated the presence of chloride, bromide, iodide, acetate, formate, chlorate and nitrate. Subsequent tests for metals will detect some negative radicals which contain metals e.g. chromates and permanganates containing chromium and manganese respectively.

### Preparing the Solution

Since the presence of the so-called *heavy metals* like silver in the sample

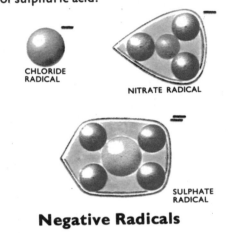

CHLORIDE RADICAL

NITRATE RADICAL

SULPHATE RADICAL

**Negative Radicals**

could interfere with the tests for negative radicals, it is necessary to remove any of them, should they be present. This is done by boiling a finely powdered portion of the sample with sodium carbonate solution and filtering off any precipitate. The filtrate contains the acid radicals originally combined with the heavy metals but now they are present as sodium salts, while the metals themselves have been precipitated as insoluble carbonates or hydroxides and retained on the filter paper. A portion of this filtrate is used for each test.

As the filtrate is certain to be alkaline (on account of the excess of sodium carbonate used in removing the heavy metals), it is necessary to add acid to neutralize the solution and convert the carbonate radical into carbon dioxide gas. If the solution is not acidified sufficiently, the addition of reagents like silver nitrate may lead to the precipitation of insoluble carbonate. However, great care must be exercised in the choice of acid – on no account should sulphuric acid be used to acidify the solution which is subsequently to be tested for the sulphate radical! The safest way of preventing this is to use the acid which contains the same acid radical as the testing reagent. If the reagent is a nitrate (e.g. silver nitrate) the solution should be acidified with nitric acid.

The need to have all glassware scrupulously clean cannot be over emphasised, for traces of other substances left behind from previous analyses can lead to all manner of false inferences. Great care must also be taken to replace the stoppers in the correct reagent bottles immediately they have been used.

### Sulphate Radical

The first portion of the filtrate is acidified with dilute hydrochloric acid and then barium chloride solution is added. If a sulphate is present this will cause the formation of white, insoluble barium sulphate. Since the other salts of barium are soluble in hydrochloric acid, the appearance of a white precipitate in this test proves the presence of the sulphate radical.

### Halide Radicals

Since the chloride, bromide and iodide of silver are all insoluble, the presence of these halides in the solution can be detected through the precipitation of the corresponding silver halide. This is done by adding first an excess of dilute nitric acid and then silver nitrate solution. The particular halide may be identified by the colour of the precipitate, and the effect of ammonium hydroxide on it.

A white curdy precipitate (silver chloride) which readily dissolves in ammonium hydroxide solution confirms the presence of a chloride radical. Precipitated silver bromide is a pale yellow, but as this coloration is sometimes very slight, the precipitate should be compared with a prepared silver chloride precipitate. Silver bromide is slightly soluble in ammonia. In contrast, precipitated silver iodide, which is yellow, is insoluble in ammonium hydroxide.

As the latter test is not conclusive proof, the presence of a bromide or iodide radical needs to be confirmed. This is done by heating a small quantity of the original substance with manganese dioxide and concentrated sulphuric acid. If there is a bromide radical in the original substance, reddish-brown bromine vapour will be seen, while an iodide will give rise to violet iodine vapour.

An indication of phosphate, arsenate, chromate, antimonate, borate and oxalate may be obtained by further treating the filtrate obtained by removing the precipitated silver halide. Ammonia is added drop by drop to this filtrate until the solution is neutral. The colour of any precipitate formed in this neutral solution is a guide to the presence of one of these radicals.

### Nitrate Radical

Another portion of the original solution is treated in the *cold*, with a slight excess of dilute sulphuric acid. The evolution of brown fumes (nitrogen dioxide) indicates the presence of a *nitrite*, in which case the solution will

| Colour of Precipitate | Inference |
|---|---|
| white | antimonate, borate or oxalate |
| yellow | phosphate |
| brick red | arsenate |
| crimson red | chromate |

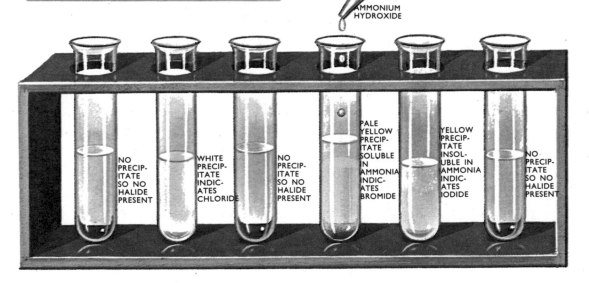

*To test for a halide, the solution is acidified with dilute nitric acid, then silver nitrate solution is added. A chloride yields a white precipitate of silver chloride (tube 2), a bromide a pale yellow precipitate of silver bromide (tube 4), and an iodide a yellow precipitate of silver iodide (tube 5). Precipitated silver bromide dissolves in ammonium hydroxide solution but silver iodide does not.*

also give a positive reaction to the nitrate test.

Ferrous sulphate solution, which must be freshly prepared, is then added to the acidified solution containing the sample. The tube containing these mixed solutions is then tilted and concentrated sulphuric acid is carefully poured in so that it forms a separate layer about 1 cm. deep at the foot of the tube. If the solution contains a nitrate, a *brown ring* will appear at the interface between the two liquid layers in the test tube.

The unstable brown compound is formed as a result of a three stage reaction. First, nitric acid is generated by the action of the concentrated sulphuric acid on the nitrate. The nitric acid is reduced to nitric oxide by some of the ferrous sulphate. This nitric oxide combines with more ferrous sulphate to form the unstable brown layer.

## Borate Radical

This test is carried out on the original substance and not on the solution from which the heavy metals have been removed. The solid is mixed with a little concentrated sulphuric acid and then stirred into some methylated spirit in an evaporating dish. The dish is then warmed and the vapour rising from it is ignited. If a borate is present, the flame is coloured green. This is due to the formation of volatile ethyl borate.

Many tests for *negative radicals* are carried out on a solution from which the heavy metals like lead and silver have been removed by treating the sample with sodium carbonate solution.

SAMPLE BOILED WITH SODIUM CARBONATE SOLUTION

CARBONATES OF HEAVY METALS RETAINED ON FILTER PAPER

NEGATIVE RADICALS IN FILTRATE AS SODIUM SALTS

*The presence of a* nitrate *is demonstrated by the brown ring test.*

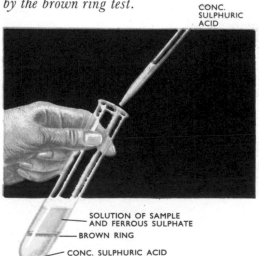

CONC. SULPHURIC ACID

SOLUTION OF SAMPLE AND FERROUS SULPHATE

BROWN RING

CONC. SULPHURIC ACID

66

# CHAPTER TWENTY-TWO

# Inorganic Group Analysis

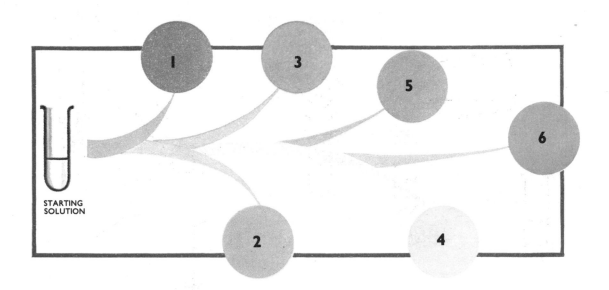

STARTING
SOLUTION

BECAUSE there are so many different metals to choose from, *inorganic group analysis* is used. This is a method devised to work equally well if all the metals are present or if there is only one of them there, and if it is performed properly even the most inconspicuous metals should be detected.

All the metallic ions are put into solution. The conditions are then altered so that most still remain in solution but a small group are thrown out as solid precipitates because the new salts formed are insoluble. These can be separated from the rest by filtration and constitute a particular group. Then the conditions are altered again so that another small group is precipitated and filtered out and another and so on until the jumbled mixture of metallic ions is sorted out into 6 groups which can easily be dealt with.

For example, there are only three really insoluble chlorides. The rest are more soluble. Insoluble ones are lead, silver and mercurous chlorides. These salts are thrown out of solution when they are formed, by the addition of dilute hydrochloric acid to a solution of some of the other salts of the metal. They can then be separated out from the other soluble chlorides by filtration. An excess of acid must be added so that all of these metallic ions are brought down as precipitates. There must be complete removal otherwise false results will be obtained during later stages of the analysis. The precipitate is known as the group 1 precipitate and the metals, the group 1 metals. At a later stage, the precipitate can be examined to find out which of these three metals it contains.

The separation of the metallic ions into groups is outlined here.

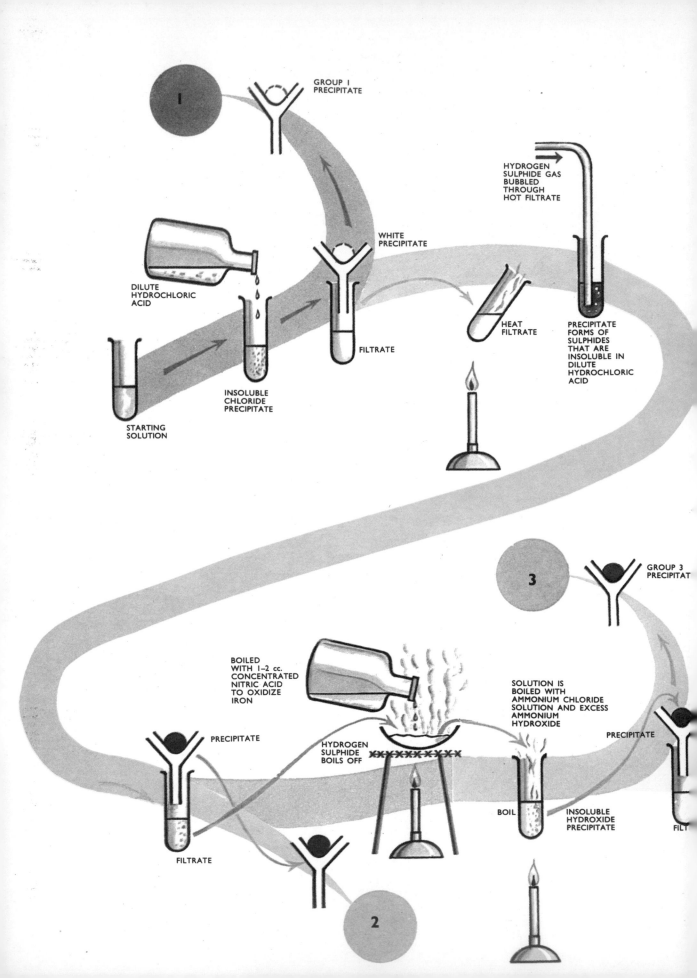

## Group 1.

LEAD, SILVER and MERCUROUS salts have been 'shunted off' because their chlorides are insoluble in cold water.
These three can be further subdivided because lead chloride is soluble in hot water and the other two are not. Silver can then be dissolved out with ammonium hydroxide solution. More tests are applied. For example, the hot lead chloride solution gives a bright yellow precipitate on addition of potassium dichromate solution. No yellow precipitate, no lead.

## Group 2.

This is a large group of metals whose sulphides are insoluble in dilute hydrochloric acid. Because this group is too large to handle, it is subdivided into two smaller groups, 2a and 2b. ARSENIC, TIN and ANTIMONY, the group 2b metals are shunted off because their sulphides dissolve in boiling sodium hydroxide solution. The group 2a metals, MERCURY, LEAD, BISMUTH, COPPER and CADMIUM are left behind.

## Group 3.

IRON, ALUMINIUM and CHROMIUM compounds are side-tracked because they form insoluble hydroxides with ammonium chloride solution and ammonia.

## Group 4.

ZINC, MANGANESE, NICKEL and COBALT are diverted because they form insoluble sulphides with ammonium hydroxide solution when hydrogen sulphide is bubbled through it. The precipitate is further separated and tested.

## Group 5.

The three chemically related elements, CALCIUM, STRONTIUM and BARIUM, are separated out as insoluble carbonates on boiling with ammonium carbonate solution.

## Group 6.

When groups 1–5 have been separated out, the group 6 metals are left behind in solution. These are MAGNESIUM, SODIUM and POTASSIUM.

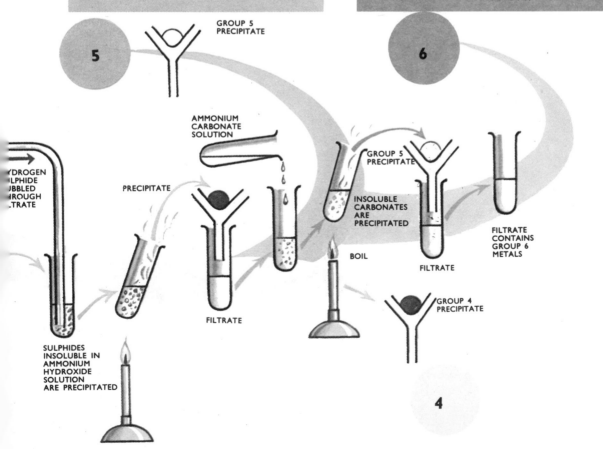

GROUP 5 PRECIPITATE

5

6

HYDROGEN SULPHIDE BUBBLED THROUGH FILTRATE

AMMONIUM CARBONATE SOLUTION

PRECIPITATE

FILTRATE

SULPHIDES INSOLUBLE IN AMMONIUM HYDROXIDE SOLUTION ARE PRECIPITATED

GROUP 5 PRECIPITATE

INSOLUBLE CARBONATES ARE PRECIPITATED

BOIL

FILTRATE

FILTRATE CONTAINS GROUP 6 METALS

GROUP 4 PRECIPITATE

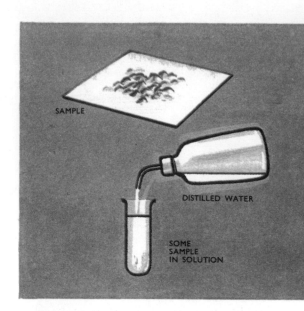

## Making a Solution

If the substance to be analyzed is a solid, it must first be put into solution. Fortunately most inorganic substances dissolve in water and it is usually not necessary to search for other solvents. Tap water should not be used for this as it contains impurities such as magnesium and calcium ions which would be detected later in the analysis, giving false results. Distilled or deionized water should be used instead.

If the substance will not dissolve in water, dilute hydrochloric acid should be tried and if this does not work, the concentrated acid probably will. (There are objections to the use of both sulphuric and nitric acids).

SAMPLE

DISTILLED WATER

SOME SAMPLE IN SOLUTION

## Precipitation

In each case, sufficient reagent must be added so that precipitation is complete. Incomplete precipitation gives rise to strange results later on.

## Washing

As all the group precipitates have some filtrate clinging to them, they must be washed free of contamination before further examination.

## SORTING OUT THE METALS—GROUP 1

THE first group of ions to be removed from the solution is known as *group* 1. Group 1 metallic ions are *lead*, *silver* and *mercurous*. Unlike all the other metals, these three form very *insoluble chlorides*. This fact is used in removing them from the other metals in solution.

When dilute hydrochloric acid is added, lead, silver and mercurous chlorides are thrown out of solution as white solids which are then filtered out. The mass of solid particles removed from the solution is known as the *group* 1 *precipitate*.

Does this group 1 precipitate consist of one, two or all three of these metals? Each chloride has different properties. The lead chloride will dissolve in water on heating and with potassium chromate solution will give a bright yellow precipitate. With ammonium hydroxide solution mercurous chloride turns black. Silver chloride, though, dissolves in ammonia, but when dilute nitric acid is added, it is precipitated again. This precipitate is sensitive to light and blackens on keeping.

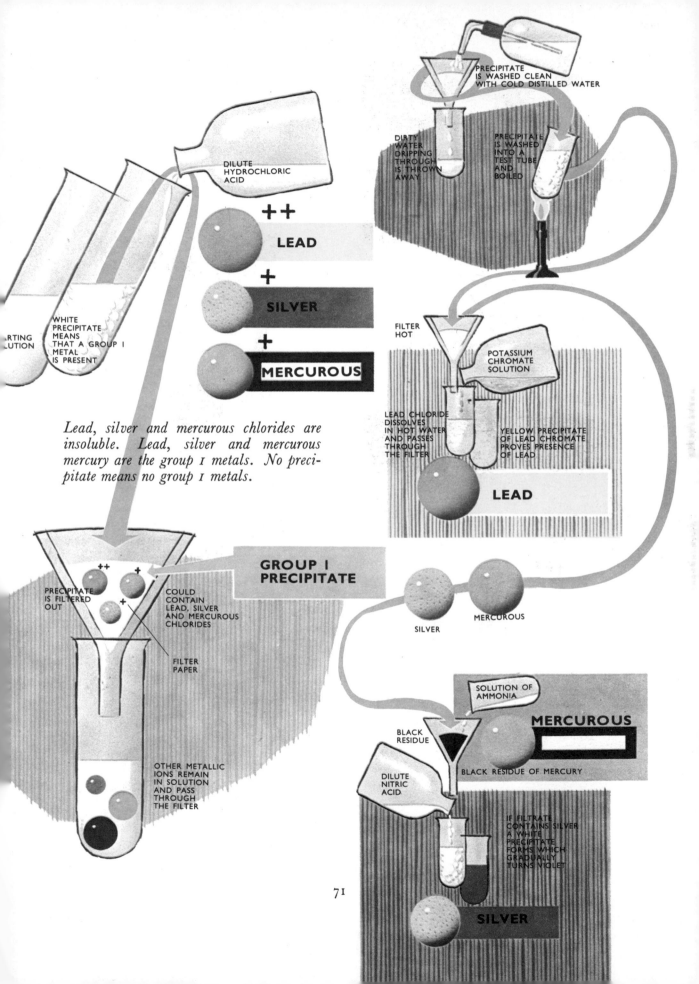

DILUTE HYDROCHLORIC ACID

++ LEAD
+ SILVER
+ MERCUROUS

...RTING ...LUTION

WHITE PRECIPITATE MEANS THAT A GROUP I METAL IS PRESENT

*Lead, silver and mercurous chlorides are insoluble. Lead, silver and mercurous mercury are the group I metals. No precipitate means no group I metals.*

PRECIPITATE IS WASHED CLEAN WITH COLD DISTILLED WATER

DIRTY WATER DRIPPING THROUGH IS THROWN AWAY

PRECIPITATE IS WASHED INTO A TEST TUBE AND BOILED

FILTER HOT

POTASSIUM CHROMATE SOLUTION

LEAD CHLORIDE DISSOLVES IN HOT WATER AND PASSES THROUGH THE FILTER

YELLOW PRECIPITATE OF LEAD CHROMATE PROVES PRESENCE OF LEAD

LEAD

GROUP I PRECIPITATE

PRECIPITATE IS FILTERED OUT

COULD CONTAIN LEAD, SILVER AND MERCUROUS CHLORIDES

FILTER PAPER

SILVER    MERCUROUS

OTHER METALLIC IONS REMAIN IN SOLUTION AND PASS THROUGH THE FILTER

SOLUTION OF AMMONIA

MERCUROUS

BLACK RESIDUE

BLACK RESIDUE OF MERCURY

DILUTE NITRIC ACID

IF FILTRATE CONTAINS SILVER A WHITE PRECIPITATE FORMS WHICH GRADUALLY TURNS VIOLET

SILVER

71

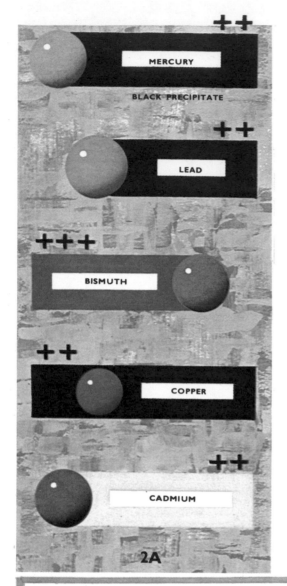

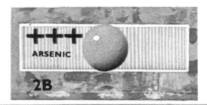

These ions are known as the group 2 ions. All of them form insoluble sulphides in acidic solution. This is used to separate them from other metallic ions. When hydrogen sulphide is bubbled through an acidic solution they come out of solution as sulphides, but the others stop in solution. When sufficient hydrogen sulphide has been bubbled through, all these ions can be filtered out and separated from the rest.

If there is only one group 2 metal present, the colour of the precipitate will give a clue to its composition. An orange precipitate means cadmium only is present. With a mixture, though, the orange colour will not be apparent.

AFTER the insoluble chlorides, the *group* 2 metals are taken out. These are the ions of mercuric mercury, lead, bismuth, copper, cadmium, arsenic, antimony and tin. All form *insoluble sulphides* in acidic solu-tions so this is used to separate them from the rest.

There are too many metals in group 2 (the largest group) to make it prac-ticable to analyse it as one group. The analysis is made simpler by splitting the group into two. Group 2A consists of the metals whose sulphides do not dissolve in caustic soda and ammonium sulphide. The rest, arsenic, antimony and tin sulphides do dissolve. They are the group 2B metals.

Each sulphide has some special property which is used to distinguish it from the rest in the group.

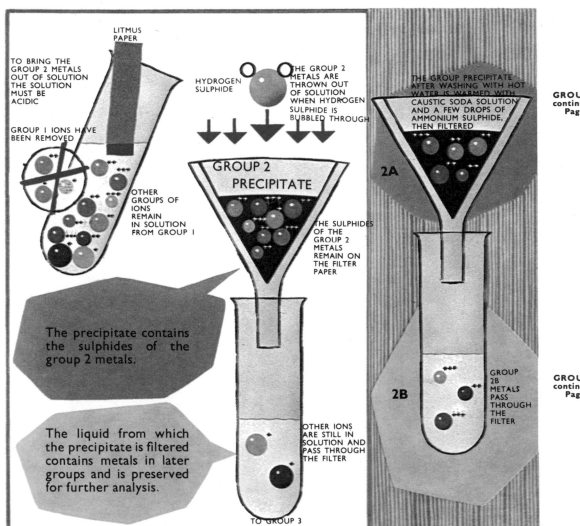

LITMUS PAPER

TO BRING THE GROUP 2 METALS OUT OF SOLUTION THE SOLUTION MUST BE ACIDIC

GROUP 1 IONS HAVE BEEN REMOVED

HYDROGEN SULPHIDE

THE GROUP 2 METALS ARE THROWN OUT OF SOLUTION WHEN HYDROGEN SULPHIDE IS BUBBLED THROUGH

OTHER GROUPS OF IONS REMAIN IN SOLUTION FROM GROUP I

GROUP 2 PRECIPITATE

THE SULPHIDES OF THE GROUP 2 METALS REMAIN ON THE FILTER PAPER

THE GROUP PRECIPITATE AFTER WASHING WITH HOT WATER IS WARMED WITH CAUSTIC SODA SOLUTION AND A FEW DROPS OF AMMONIUM SULPHIDE, THEN FILTERED

2A

GROUP 2A continued on Page 74

The precipitate contains the sulphides of the group 2 metals.

The liquid from which the precipitate is filtered contains metals in later groups and is preserved for further analysis.

OTHER IONS ARE STILL IN SOLUTION AND PASS THROUGH THE FILTER

2B

GROUP 2B METALS PASS THROUGH THE FILTER

GROUP 2B continued on Page 75

TO GROUP 3

73

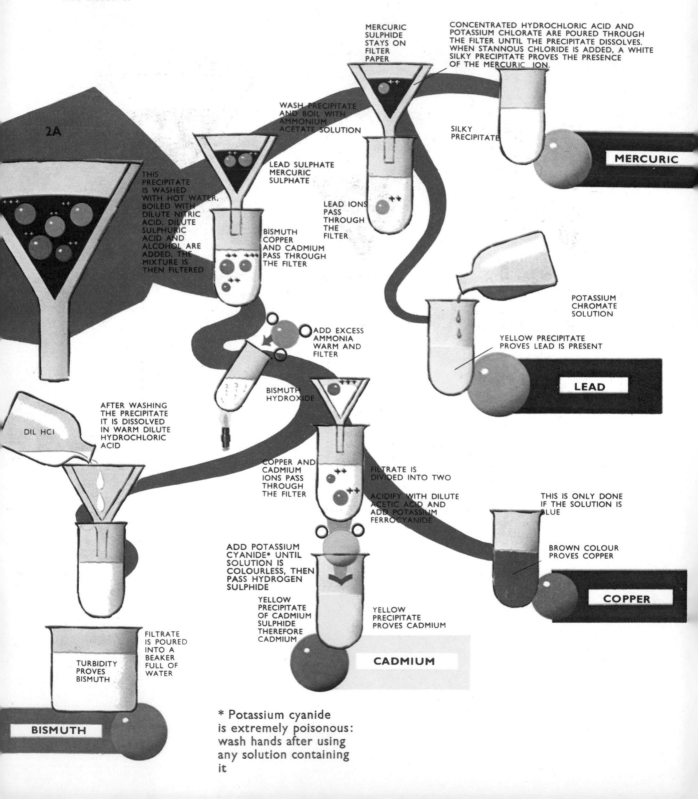

## GROUP 2A

So that the metallic ions among this possible mixture of mercuric, lead, bismuth, copper and cadmium ions can be identified, the group is again split. Bismuth and cadmium are separated from the rest by dissolving them under conditions in which the other three will not dissolve.

MERCURIC SULPHIDE STAYS ON FILTER PAPER

CONCENTRATED HYDROCHLORIC ACID AND POTASSIUM CHLORATE ARE POURED THROUGH THE FILTER UNTIL THE PRECIPITATE DISSOLVES. WHEN STANNOUS CHLORIDE IS ADDED, A WHITE SILKY PRECIPITATE PROVES THE PRESENCE OF THE MERCURIC ION.

WASH PRECIPITATE AND BOIL WITH AMMONIUM ACETATE SOLUTION

SILKY PRECIPITATE

**MERCURIC**

2A

THIS PRECIPITATE IS WASHED WITH HOT WATER, BOILED WITH DILUTE NITRIC ACID, DILUTE SULPHURIC ACID AND ALCOHOL ARE ADDED, THE MIXTURE IS THEN FILTERED

LEAD SULPHATE MERCURIC SULPHATE

LEAD IONS PASS THROUGH THE FILTER

BISMUTH COPPER AND CADMIUM PASS THROUGH THE FILTER

POTASSIUM CHROMATE SOLUTION

YELLOW PRECIPITATE PROVES LEAD IS PRESENT

**LEAD**

ADD EXCESS AMMONIA WARM AND FILTER

BISMUTH HYDROXIDE

AFTER WASHING THE PRECIPITATE IT IS DISSOLVED IN WARM DILUTE HYDROCHLORIC ACID

DIL HCl

COPPER AND CADMIUM IONS PASS THROUGH THE FILTER

FILTRATE IS DIVIDED INTO TWO

ACIDIFY WITH DILUTE ACETIC ACID AND ADD POTASSIUM FERROCYANIDE

THIS IS ONLY DONE IF THE SOLUTION IS BLUE

BROWN COLOUR PROVES COPPER

ADD POTASSIUM CYANIDE* UNTIL SOLUTION IS COLOURLESS, THEN PASS HYDROGEN SULPHIDE

YELLOW PRECIPITATE OF CADMIUM SULPHIDE THEREFORE CADMIUM

YELLOW PRECIPITATE PROVES CADMIUM

**COPPER**

**CADMIUM**

FILTRATE IS POURED INTO A BEAKER FULL OF WATER

TURBIDITY PROVES BISMUTH

**BISMUTH**

* Potassium cyanide is extremely poisonous: wash hands after using any solution containing it

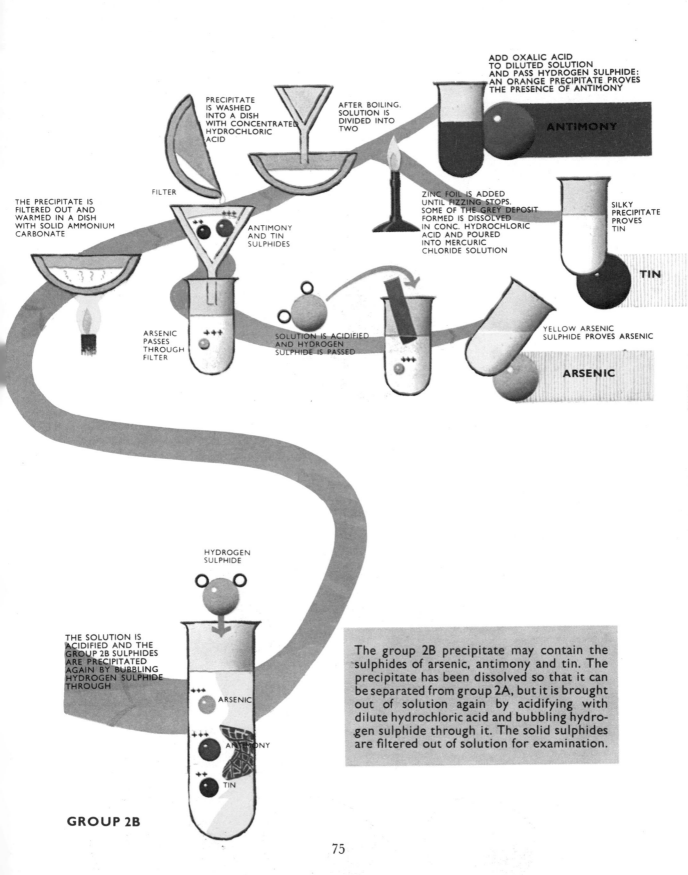

ADD OXALIC ACID
TO DILUTED SOLUTION
AND PASS HYDROGEN SULPHIDE:
AN ORANGE PRECIPITATE PROVES
THE PRESENCE OF ANTIMONY

ANTIMONY

PRECIPITATE
IS WASHED
INTO A DISH
WITH CONCENTRATED
HYDROCHLORIC
ACID

AFTER BOILING,
SOLUTION IS
DIVIDED INTO
TWO

FILTER

ZINC FOIL IS ADDED
UNTIL FIZZING STOPS.
SOME OF THE GREY DEPOSIT
FORMED IS DISSOLVED
IN CONC. HYDROCHLORIC
ACID AND POURED
INTO MERCURIC
CHLORIDE SOLUTION

SILKY
PRECIPITATE
PROVES
TIN

TIN

THE PRECIPITATE IS
FILTERED OUT AND
WARMED IN A DISH
WITH SOLID AMMONIUM
CARBONATE

ANTIMONY
AND TIN
SULPHIDES

ARSENIC
PASSES
THROUGH
FILTER

SOLUTION IS ACIDIFIED
AND HYDROGEN
SULPHIDE IS PASSED

YELLOW ARSENIC
SULPHIDE PROVES ARSENIC

ARSENIC

HYDROGEN
SULPHIDE

THE SOLUTION IS
ACIDIFIED AND THE
GROUP 2B SULPHIDES
ARE PRECIPITATED
AGAIN BY BUBBLING
HYDROGEN SULPHIDE
THROUGH

ARSENIC

ANTIMONY

TIN

The group 2B precipitate may contain the
sulphides of arsenic, antimony and tin. The
precipitate has been dissolved so that it can
be separated from group 2A, but it is brought
out of solution again by acidifying with
dilute hydrochloric acid and bubbling hydrogen sulphide through it. The solid sulphides
are filtered out of solution for examination.

GROUP 2B

IN group 3, the metallic ions separated out from the rest are those of *iron*, *chromium* and *aluminium*. They are brought out of solution under carefully regulated conditions as insoluble hydroxides. The other metallic ions present remain in solution. This enables the group 3 ions to be filtered out from the rest.

Because the three hydroxides have different chemical properties, they can be separated one from another and identified.

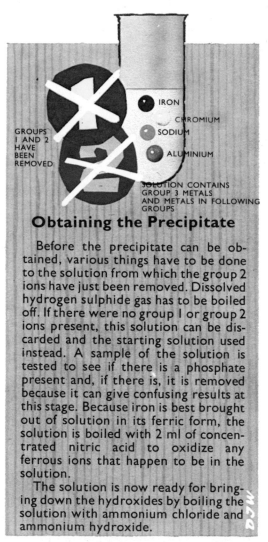

GROUPS 1 AND 2 HAVE BEEN REMOVED

IRON
CHROMIUM
SODIUM
ALUMINIUM

SOLUTION CONTAINS GROUP 3 METALS AND METALS IN FOLLOWING GROUPS

## Obtaining the Precipitate

Before the precipitate can be obtained, various things have to be done to the solution from which the group 2 ions have just been removed. Dissolved hydrogen sulphide gas has to be boiled off. If there were no group I or group 2 ions present, this solution can be discarded and the starting solution used instead. A sample of the solution is tested to see if there is a phosphate present and, if there is, it is removed because it can give confusing results at this stage. Because iron is best brought out of solution in its ferric form, the solution is boiled with 2 ml of concentrated nitric acid to oxidize any ferrous ions that happen to be in the solution.

The solution is now ready for bringing down the hydroxides by boiling the solution with ammonium chloride and ammonium hydroxide.

If there is only one group 3 metal present, the colour of the group precipitate will tell which metal it is.

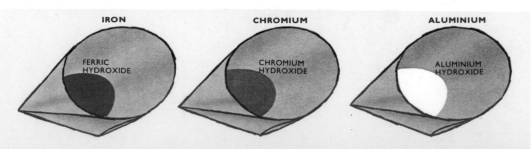

IRON — FERRIC HYDROXIDE

CHROMIUM — CHROMIUM HYDROXIDE

ALUMINIUM — ALUMINIUM HYDROXIDE

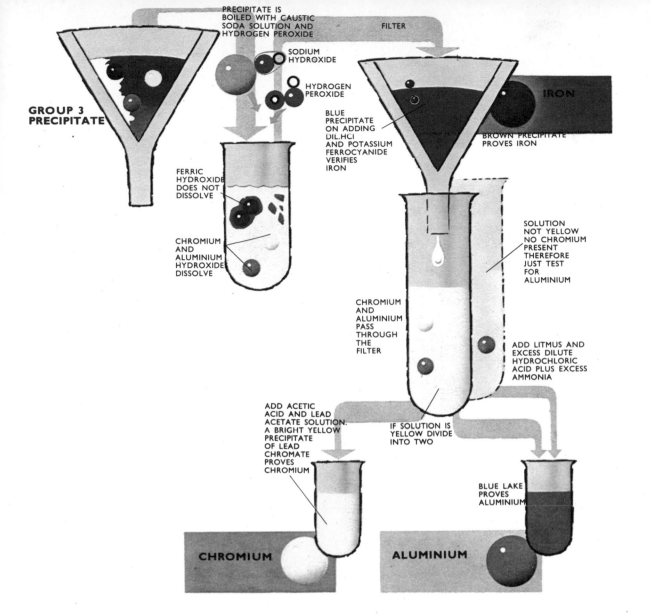

GROUP 3
PRECIPITATE

PRECIPITATE IS
BOILED WITH CAUSTIC
SODA SOLUTION AND
HYDROGEN PEROXIDE

FILTER

SODIUM
HYDROXIDE

HYDROGEN
PEROXIDE

IRON

BLUE
PRECIPITATE
ON ADDING
DIL. HCl
AND POTASSIUM
FERROCYANIDE
VERIFIES
IRON

BROWN PRECIPITATE
PROVES IRON

FERRIC
HYDROXIDE
DOES NOT
DISSOLVE

CHROMIUM
AND
ALUMINIUM
HYDROXIDE
DISSOLVE

SOLUTION
NOT YELLOW
NO CHROMIUM
PRESENT
THEREFORE
JUST TEST
FOR
ALUMINIUM

CHROMIUM
AND
ALUMINIUM
PASS
THROUGH
THE
FILTER

ADD LITMUS AND
EXCESS DILUTE
HYDROCHLORIC
ACID PLUS EXCESS
AMMONIA

ADD ACETIC
ACID AND LEAD
ACETATE SOLUTION.
A BRIGHT YELLOW
PRECIPITATE
OF LEAD
CHROMATE
PROVES
CHROMIUM

IF SOLUTION IS
YELLOW DIVIDE
INTO TWO

BLUE LAKE
PROVES
ALUMINIUM

CHROMIUM

ALUMINIUM

It is impossible to tell from the group precipitate whether
the iron was originally in the ferrous or in the ferric form.
To find out which, further tests must be made on the original
sample.

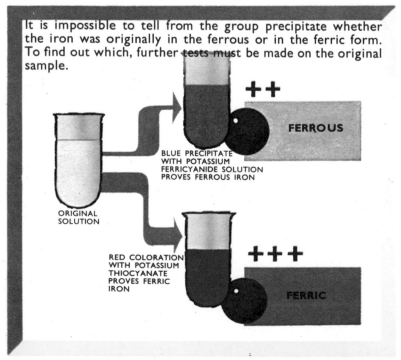

++

FERROUS

BLUE PRECIPITATE
WITH POTASSIUM
FERRICYANIDE SOLUTION
PROVES FERROUS IRON

ORIGINAL
SOLUTION

RED COLORATION
WITH POTASSIUM
THIOCYANATE
PROVES FERRIC
IRON

+++

FERRIC

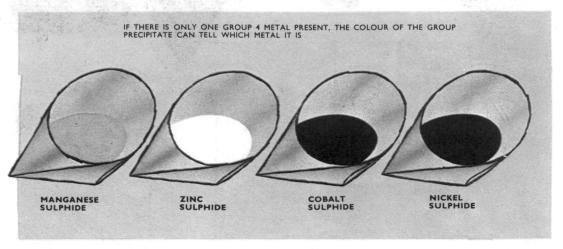

IF THERE IS ONLY ONE GROUP 4 METAL PRESENT, THE COLOUR OF THE GROUP PRECIPITATE CAN TELL WHICH METAL IT IS

MANGANESE SULPHIDE | ZINC SULPHIDE | COBALT SULPHIDE | NICKEL SULPHIDE

*Manganese sulphide is flesh coloured; zinc sulphide is white; cobalt and nickel sulphides are both black.*

BY now, three groups of metallic ions have been removed from the solution and analyzed, a group at a time.

Hydrogen sulphide, the gas that smells of bad eggs, has already been used to bring the group II ions out of solution. These sulphides were thrown out of solution in acidic conditions.

When the solution is made alkaline and hydrogen sulphide is bubbled through, four more common metallic ions are thrown out of solution as solid sulphides. They are the group IV ions. The mass of solid particles that comes out is known as the group IV precipitate. If all the group IV ions are present, it will consist of a mixture containing the sulphides of *zinc, manganese, cobalt* and *nickel*.

The colour of the precipitate can give a valuable clue to its composition. A flesh-coloured precipitate must contain manganese sulphide and a pure white precipitate will contain only zinc sulphide. If it is not black, there can be no cobalt or nickel present, for the sulphides of cobalt and nickel are both black. The precipitate now undergoes tests which use the different chemical properties of each of the four sulphides to distinguish between them.

IF BOTH NICKEL AND COBALT ARE PRESENT, THE BORAX BEAD TEST WILL NOT GIVE ANY USEFUL INFORMATION. THIS PRECIPITATE IS DISSOLVED IN AQUA REGIA NEUTRALIZED WITH SOLID SODIUM CARBONATE AND THE NEW PRECIPITATE DISSOLVED IN ACETIC ACID. SODIUM AND POTASSIUM NITRATE SOLUTIONS ARE ADDED. COBALT PRECIPITATES AS A COMPOUND, WHICH CAN BE FILTERED OUT. NICKEL STAYS IN SOLUTION. COBALT COMPOUNDS GIVE A BLUE BORAX BEAD. WITH ALKALINE DIMETHYLGLYOXIME THE NICKEL TURNS PINK.

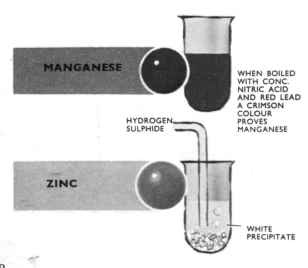

MANGANESE

ZINC

HYDROGEN SULPHIDE

WHEN BOILED WITH CONC. NITRIC ACID AND RED LEAD A CRIMSON COLOUR PROVES MANGANESE

WHITE PRECIPITATE

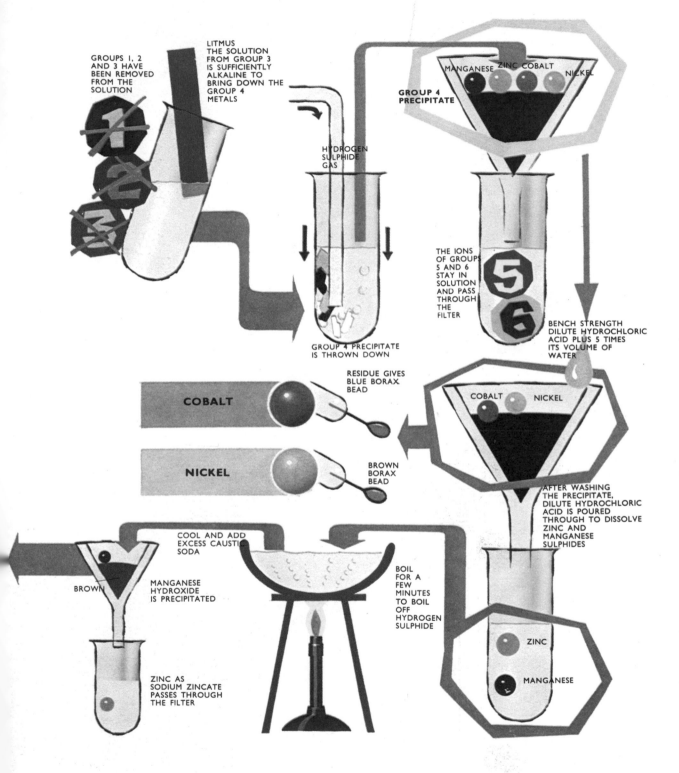

GROUPS 1, 2 AND 3 HAVE BEEN REMOVED FROM THE SOLUTION

LITMUS
THE SOLUTION FROM GROUP 3 IS SUFFICIENTLY ALKALINE TO BRING DOWN THE GROUP 4 METALS

**GROUP 4 PRECIPITATE**

MANGANESE    ZINC  COBALT    NICKEL

HYDROGEN SULPHIDE GAS

THE IONS OF GROUPS 5 AND 6 STAY IN SOLUTION AND PASS THROUGH THE FILTER

GROUP 4 PRECIPITATE IS THROWN DOWN

BENCH STRENGTH DILUTE HYDROCHLORIC ACID PLUS 5 TIMES ITS VOLUME OF WATER

RESIDUE GIVES BLUE BORAX BEAD

**COBALT**

COBALT    NICKEL

**NICKEL**

BROWN BORAX BEAD

AFTER WASHING THE PRECIPITATE, DILUTE HYDROCHLORIC ACID IS POURED THROUGH TO DISSOLVE ZINC AND MANGANESE SULPHIDES

COOL AND ADD EXCESS CAUSTIC SODA

BOIL FOR A FEW MINUTES TO BOIL OFF HYDROGEN SULPHIDE

BROWN

MANGANESE HYDROXIDE IS PRECIPITATED

ZINC

MANGANESE

ZINC AS SODIUM ZINCATE PASSES THROUGH THE FILTER

### Obtaining The Group Precipitate

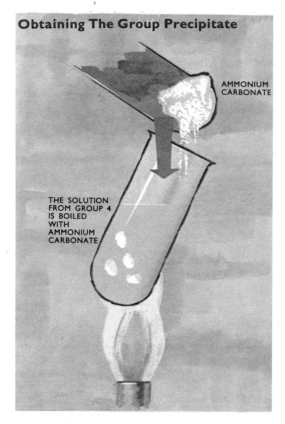

AMMONIUM CARBONATE

THE SOLUTION FROM GROUP 4 IS BOILED WITH AMMONIUM CARBONATE

THE group 5 ions are those of *calcium*, *strontium* and *barium*. The analyst will have a fairly good idea of which of these ions he expects to find. If any of them are present, this will have shown up in the flame test carried out before starting on analysis, group by group. All three metals give coloured flames. The calcium gives an orange flame, barium, apple green and strontium has a crimson flame.

The group 5 ions can be separated from those in group 6 because they form insoluble carbonates. The solution containing them is boiled with solid ammonium carbonate and the precipitate thrown out of solution is filtered out.

The precipitate is the group 5 precipitate and the liquid which drips through the filter contains only the group 6 ions. This liquid is kept so that the group 6 metals can be identified and the group 5 precipitate is examined to find what it consists of.

### GROUP PRECIPITATE

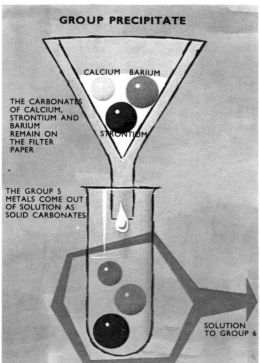

CALCIUM BARIUM

THE CARBONATES OF CALCIUM, STRONTIUM AND BARIUM REMAIN ON THE FILTER PAPER

STRONTIUM

THE GROUP 5 METALS COME OUT OF SOLUTION AS SOLID CARBONATES

SOLUTION TO GROUP 6

### Confirming The Results

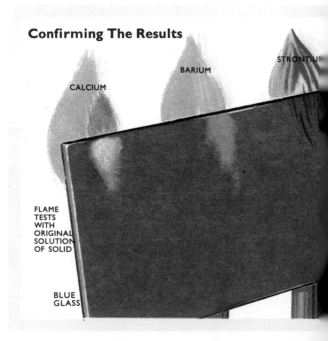

CALCIUM

BARIUM

STRONTIUM

FLAME TESTS WITH ORIGINAL SOLUTION OF SOLID

BLUE GLASS

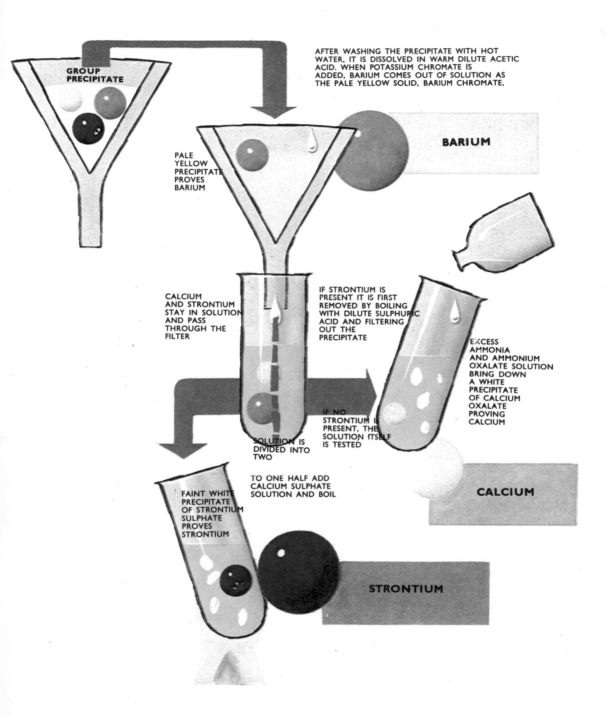

GROUP PRECIPITATE

AFTER WASHING THE PRECIPITATE WITH HOT WATER, IT IS DISSOLVED IN WARM DILUTE ACETIC ACID. WHEN POTASSIUM CHROMATE IS ADDED, BARIUM COMES OUT OF SOLUTION AS THE PALE YELLOW SOLID, BARIUM CHROMATE,

PALE YELLOW PRECIPITATE PROVES BARIUM

**BARIUM**

CALCIUM AND STRONTIUM STAY IN SOLUTION AND PASS THROUGH THE FILTER

IF STRONTIUM IS PRESENT IT IS FIRST REMOVED BY BOILING WITH DILUTE SULPHURIC ACID AND FILTERING OUT THE PRECIPITATE

EXCESS AMMONIA AND AMMONIUM OXALATE SOLUTION BRING DOWN A WHITE PRECIPITATE OF CALCIUM OXALATE PROVING CALCIUM

IF NO STRONTIUM IS PRESENT, THE SOLUTION ITSELF IS TESTED

SOLUTION IS DIVIDED INTO TWO

TO ONE HALF ADD CALCIUM SULPHATE SOLUTION AND BOIL

**CALCIUM**

FAINT WHITE PRECIPITATE OF STRONTIUM SULPHATE PROVES STRONTIUM

**STRONTIUM**

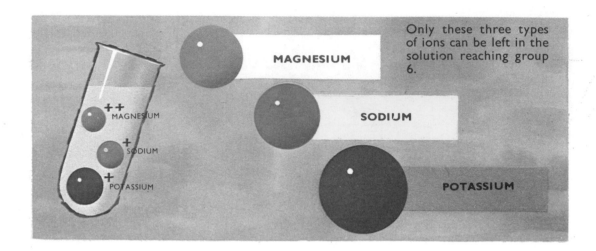

Only these three types of ions can be left in the solution reaching group 6.

MAGNESIUM

SODIUM

POTASSIUM

++ MAGNESIUM

+ SODIUM

+ POTASSIUM

BY now, five groups of ions have been removed. If this has been carried out properly, there can be only three types of metallic ions left in solution. These are the ions of group 6, *magnesium*, *sodium* and *potassium* ions. Previous groups were brought out of solution as solid precipitates because it was a good way of separating them from the rest. As these are the only three types of ions remaining, there is no point in trying to bring them out of solution. (It would be extremely difficult anyway because most salts of these ions are very soluble.)

If calcium was found in the previous group, some of it will have slipped through the net. If it is not all removed it will ruin the tests for magnesium. It can be removed by boiling the solution with a little ammonium oxalate and filtering out any solid calcium oxalate that forms.

The solution is divided into two.

One half is tested for magnesium and the other half for sodium and potassium.

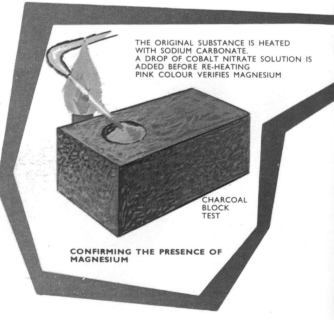

THE ORIGINAL SUBSTANCE IS HEATED WITH SODIUM CARBONATE.
A DROP OF COBALT NITRATE SOLUTION IS ADDED BEFORE RE-HEATING
PINK COLOUR VERIFIES MAGNESIUM

CHARCOAL BLOCK TEST

CONFIRMING THE PRESENCE OF MAGNESIUM

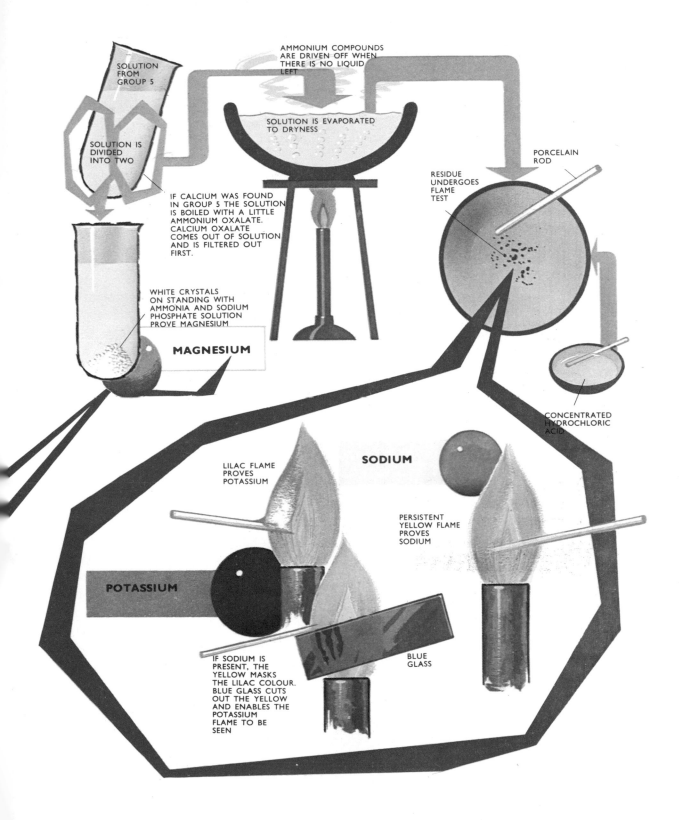

SOLUTION FROM GROUP 5

SOLUTION IS DIVIDED INTO TWO

AMMONIUM COMPOUNDS ARE DRIVEN OFF WHEN THERE IS NO LIQUID LEFT

SOLUTION IS EVAPORATED TO DRYNESS

PORCELAIN ROD

RESIDUE UNDERGOES FLAME TEST

IF CALCIUM WAS FOUND IN GROUP 5 THE SOLUTION IS BOILED WITH A LITTLE AMMONIUM OXALATE. CALCIUM OXALATE COMES OUT OF SOLUTION AND IS FILTERED OUT FIRST.

WHITE CRYSTALS ON STANDING WITH AMMONIA AND SODIUM PHOSPHATE SOLUTION PROVE MAGNESIUM

**MAGNESIUM**

CONCENTRATED HYDROCHLORIC ACID

SODIUM

LILAC FLAME PROVES POTASSIUM

PERSISTENT YELLOW FLAME PROVES SODIUM

**POTASSIUM**

IF SODIUM IS PRESENT, THE YELLOW MASKS THE LILAC COLOUR. BLUE GLASS CUTS OUT THE YELLOW AND ENABLES THE POTASSIUM FLAME TO BE SEEN

BLUE GLASS

IF a stick of white black-board chalk (calcium sulphate) is dipped into an ink-well, the ink rises up the stick as a result of capillary action. But the more striking result is that instead of the chalk's being uniformly coloured by the ink, several distinct bands of colour are to be seen along the length of the chalk. A similar effect is to be

*(Below) Apparatus in which fractions separated by column chromatography may be collected.*

COTTON WOOL PAD

SAND

COTTON WOOL

*(Right) For his experiments Tsvett used chromatographic columns like this one packed with lime or alumina.*

observed on a sheet of used blotting paper. Close examination of the larger ink blots reveals that the edges of some of the blots are of a different colour from their centres.

Many inks contain more than one dye: in some instances several dyes of different colour have been mixed to produce the required shade, while other dyes are obtained as mixtures of several coloured compounds, and no advantage is to be gained by separating them even if this were practicable. It is to be expected that such groups of compounds, some of which are rather similar in composition, have their own characteristic properties. Some have different rates of *adsorption* on to the surface of the particles of blotting paper or chalk. Thus the materials which are not readily adsorbed travel a greater distance along the chalk, or from the centre of the blot, before their motion is stopped.

Such methods of separating similar substances from a complex mixture are examples of *chromatography*. One of these techniques was used as long ago as the early years of the present century by the Russian botanist, Mikhail Semenovich Tsvett. Using petroleum as his solvent, he obtained a greenish-yellow solution of plant pigments, and set about separating the solution into its constituents by allowing it to trickle down a vertical column packed with powdered calcium carbonate.

As the solution percolated through the column, the coloration gradually extended downwards, the different coloured bands migrating at different speeds. The degree of separation was improved by washing the column with pure solvent and eventually distinct yellow and green bands corresponding to the different pigments appeared. Tsvett then allowed the solvent to drain from the column, pushed out the cylinder of calcium carbonate and cut it into portions according to the position of the coloured bands. He was then able to recover individual pigments from the various slices.

However, it was not until the 1930's that much use was made of chromatographic techniques, and it is within the past twenty years that paper chromatography, based on the ink blot observations described above, has taken its place alongside the column method developed by Tsvett.

In paper chromatography a drop of the solution to be analysed is placed near one end of a strip of adsorbent paper (e.g. filter paper). The edge of the paper is then dipped into a bath of suitable solvent. As the liquid rises up into the paper as a consequence of capillary action, the various components present in the mixture move along behind the advancing liquid. The speeds of migration depend on the chemical composition of the components. If further separation is required, the paper can be turned through a right angle so that each spot on the paper strip is spread out into a band. The pieces of paper bearing the various compounds can then be cut out and subjected to analysis.

Chromatographic techniques have been used for separating pigments, proteins, organic acids, sugars and also some of the rare earth elements into their constituents. One great advantage of these techniques, and particularly of paper chromatography, is that a separation can be performed on a very small sample.

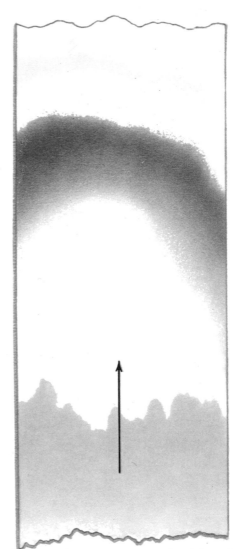

A paper chromatogram, such as that of a mixture of synthetic dyes (shown above) may be obtained using the 'ascending development' apparatus depicted below.

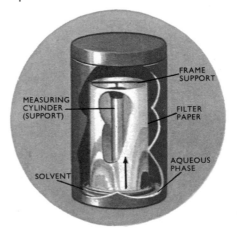

FRAME SUPPORT

MEASURING CYLINDER (SUPPORT)

FILTER PAPER

SOLVENT

AQUEOUS PHASE

IN the analysis of inorganic chemicals, one of the simplest but most positive forms of identification is the *flame test*. The unknown compound is dissolved in acid and a small quantity is picked up on a clean platinum wire. The wire is then held in a flame. If one of a number of particular metallic elements is present, the flame immediately takes on a distinctive colour – yellow for sodium, crimson for strontium, green for barium. This simple method is astonishingly sensitive – a sodium concentration of a few parts per million will give an unmistakable yellow flame, and it is used to detect all members of the group of alkali metals.

The light is given out by the flame because electrons of the atoms in the compound are *excited* by the thermal energy of the flame. The electrons are excited into higher energy electron shells, and emit light when they return to their original shells. Each particular type of electron transition give rise to light of a particular wavelength and atoms of different elements give out a particular set of different wavelengths. The result is that each element gives out a unique, easily recognised mixture of light radiations.

The simple flame test provides useful results in the laboratory, but the method can be improved upon to give even more valuable information. The simple test tells the skilled analyst, with some degree of certainty, what metal the compound contains, but it does not tell him *how much* it contains.

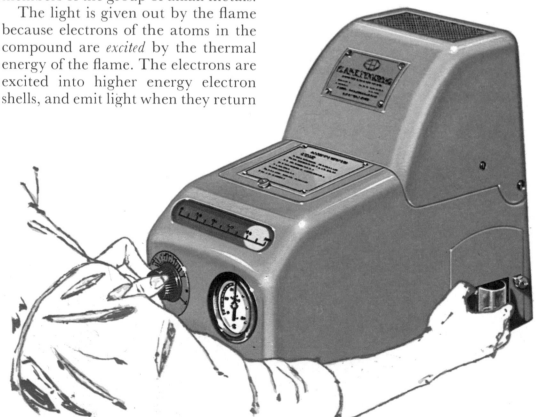

*Using a flame photometer. The solution containing the metal radicals is inserted in the beaker and when the appropriate filter is used the meter reading indicates metal concentration.*

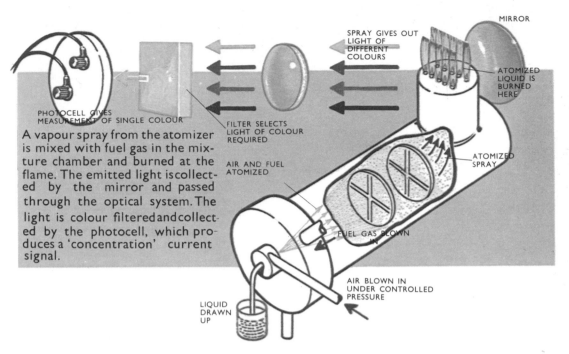

SPRAY GIVES OUT LIGHT OF DIFFERENT COLOURS

MIRROR

ATOMIZED LIQUID IS BURNED HERE

PHOTOCELL GIVES MEASUREMENT OF SINGLE COLOUR

FILTER SELECTS LIGHT OF COLOUR REQUIRED

AIR AND FUEL ATOMIZED

ATOMIZED SPRAY

FUEL GAS BLOWN IN

AIR BLOWN IN UNDER CONTROLLED PRESSURE

LIQUID DRAWN UP

A vapour spray from the atomizer is mixed with fuel gas in the mixture chamber and burned at the flame. The emitted light is collected by the mirror and passed through the optical system. The light is colour filtered and collected by the photocell, which produces a 'concentration' current signal.

The kinds of atoms present determine the *colour* of the flames, the *intensity* of the flame is determined by the number of atoms present that are emitting light of a particular colour. So, if it were possible to have a standard, steady flame fed with a steady quantity of solution, the quantity of compound present would be determined by measuring the amount of light of a particular wavelength given out by atoms of the compound. To do this, the light emitted by atoms of the particular compound needs to be isolated and then measured in intensity. This is done in a specially designed instrument – the *flame photometer*.

In the flame photometer the solution is vaporized in an *atomizer* and the droplets are fed into the fuel gas stream and carried to the burner orifice. The fuel gas can be coal gas but in some instances hydrogen-oxygen or acetylene-oxygen mixtures are used. The droplets are heated until the solvent evaporates, and the dissolved compound vaporizes. When the compound is vaporized, the atoms are excited and emit the characteristic light.

A spectral 'line' or band of a particular wavelength is isolated from the light given out. In one type of flame photometer, this is done by passing the light through an optical filter. Separate filters are provided for each of the metals to be determined – the 'sodium' filter, for example is placed in the path of the light received by the photocell when sodium content is being determined. The photocell converts the light into an electric current that is measured using a sensitive galvanometer, calibrated in terms of sodium, lithium, calcium, or potassium content, depending on the filter used.

This method provides a very sensitive measuring technique, used to measure, for example, the minute quantities of calcium in blood serum. Apart from biological applications there are many others – checking the effectiveness of water purification plant is one. Concentrations of less than one millionth of a gram per litre can be accurately measured.

*A portable pH meter being used to find the pH of the liquid in the beaker. The electrodes and platinum resistance thermometer are protected by a poly-thene sheath which can be removed when very small volumes of liquid are under test.*

RESISTANCE
THERMOMET

ELECTRODE

POLYTHE
SHEATH

# Quantitative Analysis

# CHAPTER TWENTY-THREE

# What's in a "Silver" Coin – Gravimetric Analysis

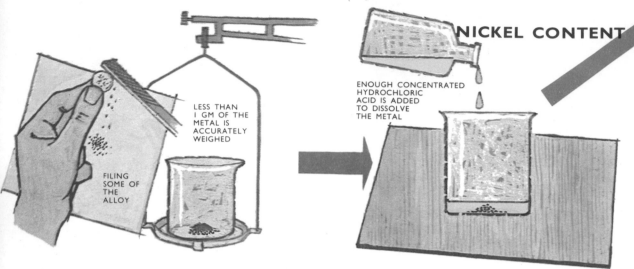

**NICKEL CONTENT**

LESS THAN 1 GM OF THE METAL IS ACCURATELY WEIGHED

FILING SOME OF THE ALLOY

ENOUGH CONCENTRATED HYDROCHLORIC ACID IS ADDED TO DISSOLVE THE METAL

SILVER coins have now been withdrawn from circulation. In most countries the present-day coins still look silvery, but like many other types of coinage they are now made from cheaper metals which have more resistance to wear and tear, often an alloy of the two metals, copper and nickel.

Analysis of such a coin involves chipping off a piece of the metal and dissolving it. Tampering with coinage in this way is illegal, but the method described here will work equally well for any piece of nickel-copper alloy.

Analysis of a metal alloy takes place in two parts. First of all, what metals are there in the alloy? Identifying the components is known as *qualitative analysis*.

But qualitative analysis does not tell how much of each metal there is in the alloy. Finding the proportions of each is known as *quantitative analysis*. Someone analyzing an alloy will be interested in the weights of each metal present. Weighing, then, is an essential feature in this analysis. The metals are separated out as compounds from each other and weighed to find out how much of each is present. Quantitative analysis based on weighing is known as *gravimetric analysis*.

Here, an alloy consisting of two metals is being examined, but the idea is exactly the same when there are

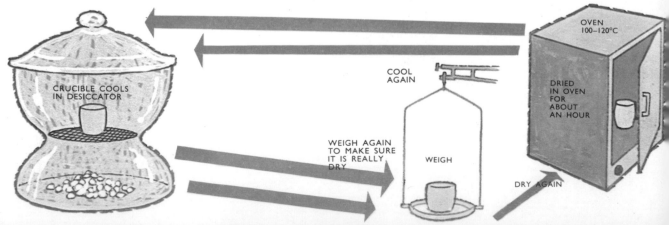

CRUCIBLE COOLS IN DESICCATOR

WEIGH AGAIN TO MAKE SURE IT IS REALLY DRY

COOL AGAIN

WEIGH

OVEN 100–120°C

DRIED IN OVEN FOR ABOUT AN HOUR

DRY AGAIN

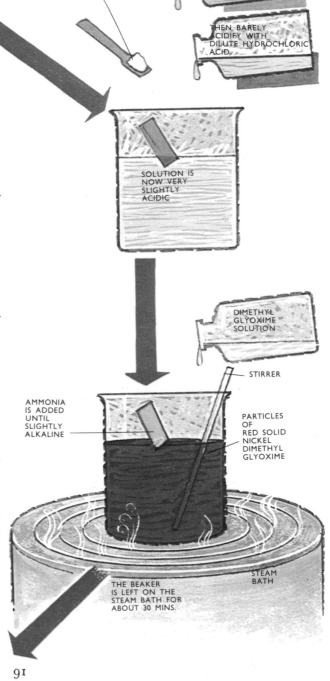

ALL METALLIC IONS ARE WASHED INTO BEAKER

THE SOLUTION IS TRANSFERRED TO THIS LARGER BEAKER WITH 200cc OF WATER

*All the nickel must be brought out of the solution as a compound and weighed. To precipitate all the nickel with dimethyl glyoxime, the solution must be carefully adjusted.*

NEUTRALIZE WITH AMMONIA

5 gm CITRIC ACID

THEN BARELY ACIDIFY WITH DILUTE HYDROCHLORIC ACID

SOLUTION IS NOW VERY SLIGHTLY ACIDIC

DIMETHYL GLYOXIME SOLUTION

STIRRER

AMMONIA IS ADDED UNTIL SLIGHTLY ALKALINE

PARTICLES OF RED SOLID NICKEL DIMETHYL GLYOXIME

STEAM BATH

THE BEAKER IS LEFT ON THE STEAM BATH FOR ABOUT 30 MINS.

many more present. Then there are just more steps to the process.

A metallic sample is completely dissolved. Ions of each metal are wandering around in the solution. The ions must be brought out of the solution, one type at a time. The reagent has been chosen to react with the ions of one metal only. It reacts with those ions and forms a compound that is *very insoluble*. The compound can no longer stay in solution so it forms particles instead. It is an easy step to filter out these particles and wash back any droplets of liquid containing ions of the other metal. If these are not washed back, some of the other metals are lost.

The reagents used for precipitating metals have been very carefully chosen. They must bring out of solution all of one metal and none of the others. A reagent must form a very insoluble compound, otherwise some of the metal will remain in solution and will not be accounted for. Compounds known as *complexes* are often used as the

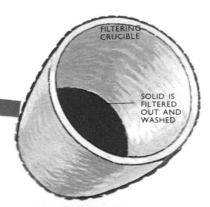

FILTERING CRUCIBLE

SOLID IS FILTERED OUT AND WASHED

91

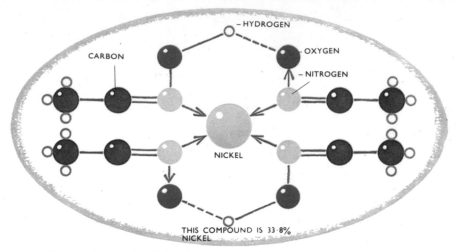

- HYDROGEN

CARBON

- OXYGEN

- NITROGEN

NICKEL

THIS COMPOUND IS 33·8% NICKEL

*Composition of Nickel Dimethyl Gloxime (see previous page).*

precipitates in gravimetric analysis. With the particular reagent the metal forms a large complex molecule – a molecule which because of its size and non-ionic structure is very insoluble.

When the complex or ordinary precipitate has been filtered out and washed clean with great care so that not one particle is lost, it must be weighed to find out how much there is of it. It cannot be weighed in its present state as it is soaking wet and the weight would be meaningless. Water would account for a good part of the weight. Every drop of water

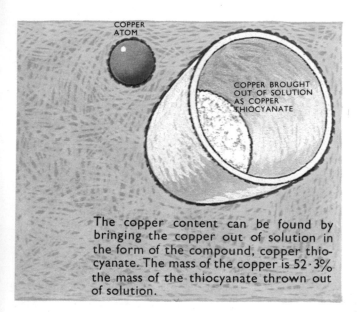

COPPER ATOM

COPPER BROUGHT OUT OF SOLUTION AS COPPER THIOCYANATE

The copper content can be found by bringing the copper out of solution in the form of the compound, copper thiocyanate. The mass of the copper is 52·3% the mass of the thiocyanate thrown out of solution.

must be driven off, but in such a way that none of the precipitate disintegrates. The vessel containing the precipitate is placed in a thermostatically controlled oven set at a moderate temperature and left to dry out for several hours. Even after a very long while in the oven the precipitate might not be properly dry. Inaccurate results will be obtained from weighing a wet precipitate. The dryness can be checked by cooling and weighing the vessel and putting it back in the oven for a few minutes more to see if the two readings coincide.

Naturally, it is wrong to carefully dry out the precipitate and then let more water creep in during the cooling before weighing. Tongs transfer the precipitate from the oven to a *desiccator* (a closed vessel containing drying agents) to cool in the dry.

The whole of gravimetric analysis depends on getting some very accurate weighings. Gravimetric analysis is not slapdash chemistry. Nothing must be spilt. No particle of precipitate must be lost. A vessel to be weighed must be handled with tongs or tweezers so that no grease and dust from the surroundings clings to the vessel and makes it heavier.

In this copper-nickel analysis, the

copper is brought out of solution as cuprous thiocyanate, CuCNS adding sulphurous acid and a 10% solution of ammonium thiocyanate. The precipitate is dried in an oven at a temperature of between 110°C and 120°C.

The nickel is made to form a complex compound with a reagent called dimethyl glyoxime. The nickel is brought out of solution as a scarlet solid.

This precipitate [formula Ni $(C_4H_7O_2N_2)_2$] is dried at the same temperature as the copper precipitate and weighed in the same way. From this weighing and the percentage of nickel in the complex the amount of nickel present can be worked out.

The coin analysed was 75% copper and 25% nickel and looked silvery even though there was three times as much copper as nickel.

CHAPTER TWENTY-FOUR

# pH Acidity

THE addition of a drop of litmus indicator to a solution will tell roughly whether it is acidic, alkaline or neutral. An acidic solution turns red, an alkaline one blue whereas a neutral solution gives a purple coloration (a mixture of red and blue).

But there are degrees of acidity and alkalinity that do not show up from such tests. One acid solution may have much greater acidity than another. For example, concentrated sulphuric acid is much more acidic than lemon juice. A concentrated solution of caustic soda is much more alkaline than a very weak solution.

pH is a measure of just how acidic or alkaline a solution is. pH values are expressed on a scale of 0 to 14. A solution with a pH of 0 is one of extreme acidity. One with pH of 1, although still strongly acidic, is slightly weaker. pH values of 2, 3, 4, 5, and 6 indicate successively weaker acidic solutions. Neutral liquids such as pure water have a pH value of 7. pH numbers from 7 to 14 indicate alkaline solutions with 14 as the extreme alkalinity.

| HYDROGEN ION CONCENTRATION IN MOLES PER LITRE | | pH | |
|---|---|---|---|
| 1 | or $10^0$ | 0 | |
| $\frac{1}{10}$ | or $10^{-1}$ | 1 | |
| $\frac{1}{100}$ | or $10^{-2}$ | 2 | |
| $\frac{1}{1,000}$ | or $10^{-3}$ | 3 | ACIDIC |
| $\frac{1}{10,000}$ | or $10^{-4}$ | 4 | |
| $\frac{1}{100,000}$ | or $10^{-5}$ | 5 | |
| $\frac{1}{1,000,000}$ | or $10^{-6}$ | 6 | |
| $\frac{1}{10,000,000}$ | or $10^{-7}$ | 7 | NEUTRAL |
| $\frac{1}{100,000,000}$ | or $10^{-8}$ | 8 | |
| $\frac{1}{1,000,000,000}$ | or $10^{-9}$ | 9 | |
| $\frac{1}{10,000,000,000}$ | or $10^{-10}$ | 10 | |
| $\frac{1}{100,000,000,000}$ | or $10^{-11}$ | 11 | ALKALINE |
| $\frac{1}{1,000,000,000,000}$ | or $10^{-12}$ | 12 | |
| $\frac{1}{10,000,000,000,000}$ | or $10^{-13}$ | 13 | |
| $\frac{1}{100,000,000,000,000}$ | or $10^{-14}$ | 14 | |

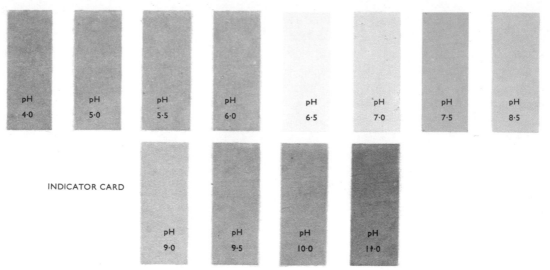

| | | | | | | | |
|---|---|---|---|---|---|---|---|
| pH 4·0 | pH 5·0 | pH 5·5 | pH 6·0 | pH 6·5 | pH 7·0 | pH 7·5 | pH 8·5 |

INDICATOR CARD

| | | | |
|---|---|---|---|
| pH 9·0 | pH 9·5 | pH 10·0 | pH 11·0 |

*A typical 'mixed indicator' card. Solutions containing a drop of indicator are matched against the card to find the pH.*

The pH values 0 to 14 are not just arbitrarily chosen numbers but do have a scientific meaning. The acidity of a solution and its pH depend on the concentration of hydrogen ions in the solution. Pure water consists mostly of water molecules and a few ions caused by the splitting of molecules into an equal number of hydrogen and hydroxyl ions. In one litre of water there are $\dfrac{1}{10,000,000}$ or $10^{-7}$ moles of hydrogen ions. A mole is a molecular weight expressed in grams. The pH with this hydrogen ion concentration is 7. If the concentration were $\dfrac{1}{1,000,000}$ or $10^{-6}$ moles

*Solutions being tested for pH with the indicator bromocresol green.*

BROMOCRESOL GREEN

| | | |
|---|---|---|
| pH BELOW 3·8 | pH OF 4·6 | pH ABOVE 5·4 |

per litre, then the pH would be 6. If it were $\dfrac{1}{100}$ or $10^{-2}$ then the pH would be 2.

The pH value of the soil is important. Although plants such as rhododendrons grow well in acid soils, most crops do very badly. They prefer soils which are neutral or slightly alkaline (pH 7–8). Soil testing outfits are used to find soil pH. If the soil is too acidic, lime corrects this. It is just as bad for the plants if this is overdone, for if the pH rises above 8 then the soil will be too alkaline for proper plant growth. For the human body to function properly the blood should have a pH of around 7·4 (very slightly alkaline). Gastric juices should have the strongly acidic value of around 2.

Indicators are dyes which change colour over a certain range of pH. Litmus passes through such a wide range of pH during its colour change that it is useless for assessing pH values. In a very acidic solution, pH 1, the indicator thymol blue is red in colour. At a pH of 1·2 it

94

begins to change colour. When the pH of 2·8 is reached the colour has completely changed to yellow. Midway between the two values, *i.e.* at pH 2, the colour is orange. Another indicator, bromocresol green, changes colour from yellow to blue in the pH range from 3·8–5·4. This indicator is green around a pH of 4·6. There is a series of indicators to show the pH value throughout the complete range from 0 to 14. Some chemical firms have brought out 'mixed indicators' which produce different colours for different pH values. For example, one 'mixed indicator' may be pink at pH 4, yellow at pH 6, green at pH 7, blue at pH 9·5 and purple at pH 11. 'Mixed indicators' are made from suitable mixtures of many indicators.

There are also meters designed to read pH values very accurately.

# CHAPTER TWENTY-FIVE

# Normal Solutions

TERMS like *dilute*, *strong* or *saturated* are often used to indicate the approximate strength of solutions. However, these vague terms are not always acceptable. When a chemical compound is manufactured, the quantities of the reactants need to be measured out quite accurately for this is no chance process. Exactly the right quantities must be mixed so that everything is used up and neither of the original substances remains in solution.

Whereas a solid can be weighed, it is not sufficient to know the volume of a solution. The *concentration* of the solution – the weight of substance dissolved in the liquid – must also be known. Although it is an easy matter to make up a solution so that one litre contains a certain weight of solid, this is not the best way to express the concentration of the solution.

When hydrochloric acid is added to a solution of potassium hydroxide (caustic potash), a molecule of each substance reacts to form a single molecule of potassium chloride. Since a molecule of hydrogen chloride (36·5 units) is lighter than one of potassium hydroxide (56·0 units) it follows that a greater mass of potassium hydroxide must be used if the maximum quantity of potassium chloride is to be made. This can be achieved by using a larger volume of potassium hydroxide assuming the concentration of the two solutions (in gm/litre) is the same.

A more satisfactory arrangement is to make up the two solutions so that they have the same number of molecules in them. Thus neither of these substances would be left over if equal volumes of the two solutions were mixed.

Solutions like these, which contain *one gram equivalent* of the substance in a litre of solution are said to be *normal*. And if equal volumes of an appropriate pair of normal solutions are mixed together both substances will be used up and there will be none of either left over. This is one of the fundamental ideas behind an important system of quantitative analysis known as *volumetric analysis*.

It is not always convenient, indeed it may not be possible, because of low solubilities, to prepare normal solu-

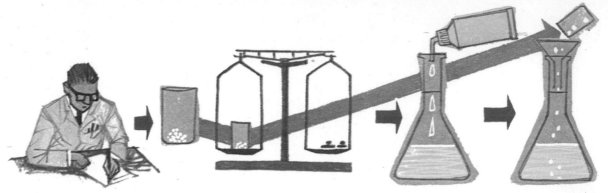

## Preparing a Standard Solution

Any solution whose concentration is accurately known is said to be *a standard solution*. It can be used to find the concentration of other solutions with which it reacts. Volumetric analysis is generally carried out with decinormal (0.1 N) solutions. The first stage in making a standard solution is to work out the gram equivalent weight of the substance. To do this the gram molecular weight is found by adding up the atomic weights of the various atoms in the molecule. The reactions in which the substance takes part will indicate the relationship between the gram equivalent weight and the gram molecular weight.

If a decinormal solution is to be made, one tenth of the gram equivalent of the substance is weighed out into a tared weighing bottle. A clean one-litre measuring flask is then partly filled with distilled water. The crystals of the substance are then carefully transferred to the flask (without losing any on the way). The flask is then shaken to dissolve the crystals which should be fairly small in size. When they have all dissolved, more distilled water is added until the liquid level corresponds with the one mark etched in the neck of the flask.

It is not possible to make up standard solutions of all substances in this way. For instance, concentrated sulphuric acid almost certainly contains some water, while pellets of sodium hydroxide actually absorb water while they are being weighed. So to obtain standard solutions of these substances, solutions of about the correct concentration are prepared. The exact concentration is then found by titrating with a solution whose concentration is accurately known.

ETCHED
MARK

tions. Volumetric analysis is often carried out with solutions which are only one tenth as concentrated. These solutions are said to be decinormal, or more frequently $0.1$ N or $\frac{1}{10}$N.

---

**To prepare 0·1 N sodium carbonate (Na$_2$CO$_3$)**

Gram molecular weight $= 2 \times 23\cdot0$ (sodium) $+ 12\cdot0$ (carbon) $+ 3 \times 16\cdot0$ (oxygen)
$$= 46\cdot0 + 12\cdot0 + 48\cdot0 = 106\cdot0 \text{ gm.}$$
But two molecules of hydrochloric acid react with one of sodium carbonate, so gram equivalent weight is half the gram molecular weight ($= 53\cdot0$ gm). So to make one litre of deci-normal solution $5\cdot30$ gm of anhydrous sodium carbonate is required. If 250 ml of solution is all that is needed $\frac{1}{4} \times 5\cdot30$ gm $= 1\cdot325$ gm of solid is used. Due allowance must be made in calculating the equivalent weight if there are molecules of water of crystallization associated with each molecule of the substance.

# CHAPTER TWENTY-SIX

# Acid Alkali Titrations

WHEN a new substance is to be made by a chemical reaction, it is best to use exactly the right amounts of the reactants, so that all are consumed and nothing is left over. If the reactants are solid, the correct quantities can be measured out by weighing. Quite often, however, the substances are available in solution, and although a certain volume of the solution can be measured out easily, this could contain almost any amount of the required reactant.

It is much more difficult to measure the amount of substance dissolved in a liquid, than it is to weigh a solid. In some instances it would be possible to evaporate a certain quantity of the solution and then weigh the residual solid. However, a much more satisfactory method of estimating the amount of the substance in solution is to find how much of this solution is required to react completely with a certain quantity of another solution whose concentration is known. (Such

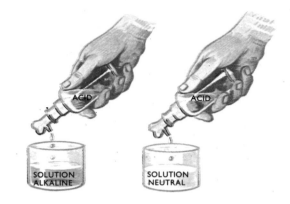

*As soon as the sodium hydroxide solution has been neutralized by the acid, the phenolphthalein indicator changes from pink to colourless.*

a solution is called a *standard* solution.) But for this method to succeed, it is necessary to know when sufficient of the second reactant has been added to react completely with the first substance.

If some dilute sodium hydroxide solution (alkaline) is put into a conical flask together with a few drops of phenolphthalein, the solution becomes pink in colour. If dilute hydrochloric

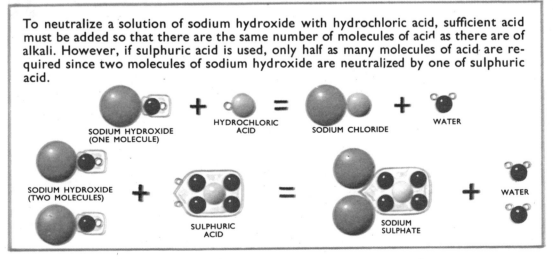

To neutralize a solution of sodium hydroxide with hydrochloric acid, sufficient acid must be added so that there are the same number of molecules of acid as there are of alkali. However, if sulphuric acid is used, only half as many molecules of acid are required since two molecules of sodium hydroxide are neutralized by one of sulphuric acid.

SODIUM HYDROXIDE (ONE MOLECULE) + HYDROCHLORIC ACID = SODIUM CHLORIDE + WATER

SODIUM HYDROXIDE (TWO MOLECULES) + SULPHURIC ACID = SODIUM SULPHATE + WATER

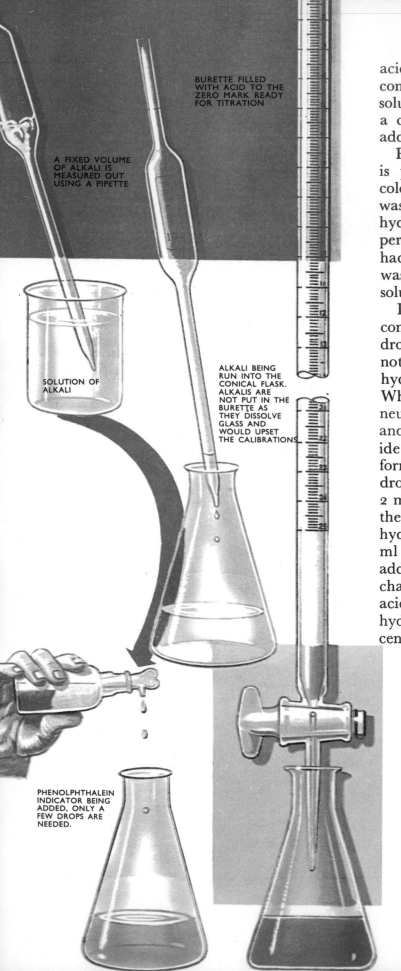

**BURETTE FILLED WITH ACID TO THE ZERO MARK READY FOR TITRATION**

**A FIXED VOLUME OF ALKALI IS MEASURED OUT USING A PIPETTE**

**SOLUTION OF ALKALI**

**ALKALI BEING RUN INTO THE CONICAL FLASK. ALKALIS ARE NOT PUT IN THE BURETTE AS THEY DISSOLVE GLASS AND WOULD UPSET THE CALIBRATIONS**

**PHENOLPHTHALEIN INDICATOR BEING ADDED, ONLY A FEW DROPS ARE NEEDED.**

acid is added slowly to the liquid in the conical flask, the colour of the mixed solution will suddenly disappear after a certain amount of acid has been added.

Phenolphthalein is an *indicator* – it is pink in alkaline solution but is colourless in acid solution. While there was an excess of the alkali (sodium hydroxide) in the flask the pink colour persisted, but as soon as all the alkali had reacted with the acid, and there was a very slight excess of acid, the solution became colourless.

If the solution in the conical flask contains 1,000 molecules of sodium hydroxide, the colour of the solution will not change until 1,000 molecules of hydrochloric acid have been added. When this happens the solution will be neutral (i.e. neither acid nor alkaline) and 1,000 molecules of sodium chloride (common salt) will have been formed. The required number of hydrochloric acid molecules may be in 2 ml, 20 ml, or 200 ml of solution. If there are 1,000 molecules of sodium hydroxide in 20 ml of solution and 200 ml of hydrochloric acid have to be added for the colour of the solution to change (i.e. for 1,000 molecules of acid to be supplied), then the sodium hydroxide solution is ten times as concentrated as the hydrochloric acid.

*As caustic alkalis tend to attack glass, they are usually put in the conical flask. A fixed volume (e.g. 10 ml or 25 ml) is, therefore, measured out carefully using a pipette. After the solution has drained into the flask a few drops of indicator (phenolphthalein) are added.*

There are, of course, far more molecules of a substance in solution than the above description suggests. In fact 1 ml of the *dilute* hydrochloric acid found on the *bench* of any laboratory contains about 1,200,000,000,000,000,000,000 molecules. As this is such a large number, a simpler method of describing the concentration of a solution is used, but it still gives a direct indication of the number of molecules (not the number of grams) of the substance which there are in a certain volume (1 litre) of the solution.

The concentrations of all solutions are related to a *normal solution – one litre* of a normal solution contains the *gram equivalent weight* of the substance. For hydrochloric acid (HCl), with one hydrogen atom in each molecule, the gram equivalent weight is the same as the gram molecular weight [1 (1 hydrogen atom) + 35·5 (1 chlorine atom) = 36·5], so that a normal solution of hydrochloric acid contains 36·5 gm per litre.

However, since each molecule of sulphuric acid ($H_2SO_4$) contains two hydrogen atoms, 500 molecules of this acid will neutralize 1,000 molecules of sodium hydroxide. The equivalent weight of sulphuric acid is, therefore, half its molecular weight [2 (2 hydrogen atoms) + 32 (1 sulphur atom) + 64 (4 oxygen atoms) = 98], so a normal solution of sulphuric acid contains 49 gm of acid per litre.

This system has the great advantage that once the concentration or *normality* of the solution is known, it is an easy matter to find how much of one solution is required to neutralize another solution. For instance 20 ml of normal (or 1N) hydrochloric acid will neutralize either 20 ml of 1N sodium hydroxide, or 10 ml of 2N sodium hydroxide or 200 ml of 0·1N sodium hydroxide. Each of these three quantities contains the same number of molecules of sodium hydroxide and is just sufficient to neutralize the hydrochloric acid solution.

This is the basis of the technique known as *volumetric analysis*, namely a means of finding the concentrations of solutions provided the concentration of one is known. Here

*After the burette has been filled with the acid solution, the liquid level is noted. Acid is then run slowly into the flask which is swirled all the time to ensure good mixing. As the end point is approached, the pink colour fades, but at the end point the solution suddenly becomes colourless. The final burette reading is noted and the volume of acid used is calculated.*

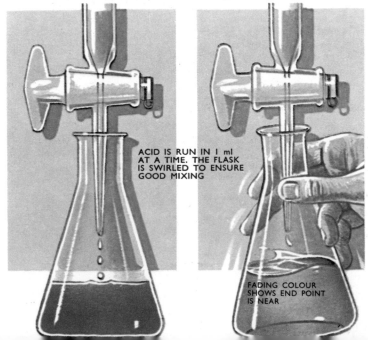

ACID IS RUN IN 1 ml
AT A TIME. THE FLASK
IS SWIRLED TO ENSURE
GOOD MIXING

FADING COLOUR
SHOWS END POINT
IS NEAR

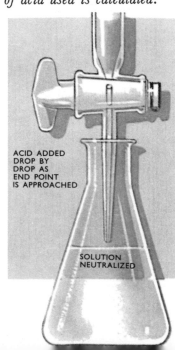

ACID ADDED
DROP BY
DROP AS
END POINT
IS APPROACHED

SOLUTION
NEUTRALIZED

## Cleanliness

The need for scrupulously clean glassware is even more important in volumetric analysis than in other branches of chemistry. Not only can the presence of other substances upset the chemical reactions, but traces of grease in the burette or pipette can lead to false readings because the *meniscus* (curved surface of the liquid) is not properly formed. Volumetric apparatus should be washed carefully each time it is used. Periodic cleaning with chromic acid is recommended as a further precaution.

## Indicators

An indicator is a substance which shows by means of a sharp change in colour that a chemical reaction is complete. Phenolphthalein, methyl red and methyl orange are used most frequently to find the end point in acid-alkali titrations. Different indicators are used in other branches of volumetric analysis.

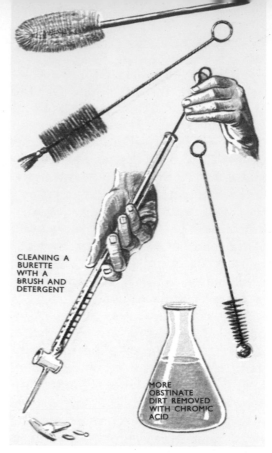

CLEANING A BURETTE WITH A BRUSH AND DETERGENT

MORE OBSTINATE DIRT REMOVED WITH CHROMIC ACID

### Typical Results of Acid-Alkali Titration

| | |
|---|---|
| Weight of weighing bottle + sodium carbonate (anhydrous) | 7·529 gm |
| Weight of weighing bottle alone | 6·288 gm |
| Weight of sodium carbonate (anhydrous) | 1·241 gm |

5·30 gm sodium carbonate (anhydrous) per litre is $0·100$ N

1·00 gm sodium carbonate (anhydrous) per 250 ml is $\dfrac{0·100 \times 4}{5·30}$ N

1·241 gm sodium carbonate (anhydrous) per 250 ml is $\dfrac{0·100 \times 4 \times 1·241}{5·30}$ N

$$= 0·0936 \text{ N}$$

This standard solution of sodium carbonate is then titrated against a solution of hydrochloric acid of unknown strength. The acid solution is put in the burette while 25·0 ml portions of the standard solution are measured into conical flasks using a pipette.

| Burette Readings | Rapid Reading | | Accurate Readings | |
|---|---|---|---|---|
| Second level | 26·1 | 48·1 | 24·2 | 46·1 |
| First level | 3·7 | 26·1 | 2·3 | 24·2 |
| Volume used (ml) | 22·4 | 22·0 | 21·9 | 21·9 |

25 ml of 0·0936 N sodium carbonate = 25 ml of 0·0936 N hydrochloric acid.

= 1 ml of $25 \times 0·0936$ N hydrochloric acid.

= 21·9 ml of $\dfrac{25 \times 0·0936}{21·9}$ N hydrochloric acid.

= 21·9 ml of **0·107 N** hydrochloric acid.

The hydrochloric acid is 0·107 N and can now be used to find the strength of various alkaline solutions.

we are concerned only with acids and alkalis but there are a number of other solutions which can be examined by a similar procedure.

The actual process of finding how much acid will react with a certain quantity of alkali is called a *titration*. The acid is usually placed in a burette (a graduated tube with a tap at the foot), while the alkali is measured out into a conical flask. A fixed quantity of alkali (10 ml, 20 ml, or 50 ml) is usually measured out using a pipette.

After the indicator has been added, small quantities of acid are run into the conical flask from the burette. After each addition of acid (about 1 ml at a time in the first titration) the liquid in the flask is swirled round to ensure that acid and alkali have been properly mixed. When sufficient acid to neutralize the alkali has been added, the colour of the solution changes in a trice – one second the solution is pink and in the next it is colourless.

The quantity of acid added is found from the burette readings. This first amount is only approximate and several further titrations are performed using fresh solution each time. The procedure for these subsequent titrations is different. The first one will have shown within 1 ml how much acid is needed to neutralize the alkali, so much more care will be taken in adding acid as the *end point* is approached. It should be possible to titrate to the nearest drop (about 0·05 ml).

The equivalent volumes of acid and alkali are now known so that the concentration of the second solution can be found provided the concentration of the first is known. A stock of standard solutions is kept in most laboratories for this purpose. The method of calculating the concentration of the second solution is quite straightforward (see the example).

# CHAPTER TWENTY-SEVEN

# How Acidic is it? pH Meters

CHEESE makers often use pH meters because the pH alters as the cheese matures. By checking the pH of the cheese at intervals its maturity can be followed.

So many of the industrial uses of pH meters are of this type. The pH readings are unimportant in themselves but give a picture of what is happening within the solution. There are, in fact, innumerable different ways in which this meter can be used to follow a reaction of some sort. It can be used to follow the resistance of teeth to acid attack, and to discover whether toilet soap is too alkaline. Very alkaline soap is harmful to the skin. The meter can also be used to regulate the amount of borax put into soap to make it less alkaline. pH meters are also used to test and adjust the acidity of swimming baths.

The treatment of effluent, the waste material from factories, is one of the most important industrial uses of pH meters. In most countries it is against the law to tip strong acids and alkalis down drains and into rivers. The effluent must be neutralized first. The machine adding the lime or neutralizing chemical is connected via an automatic controller

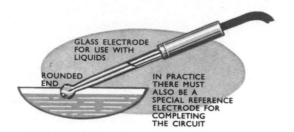

*The design of the electrodes depends very much on how they are to be used. Round ends are used for liquids; cheese testing electrodes have spear-shaped heads.*

to a pH meter dipping in some liquid channelled off from the main stream. When the reading on the meter drops below a certain value and the waste material becomes too acidic, a valve opens and allows more lime into the liquid flow.

Actually, far more pH meters are sold to research laboratories than to industry. Many are used to help with

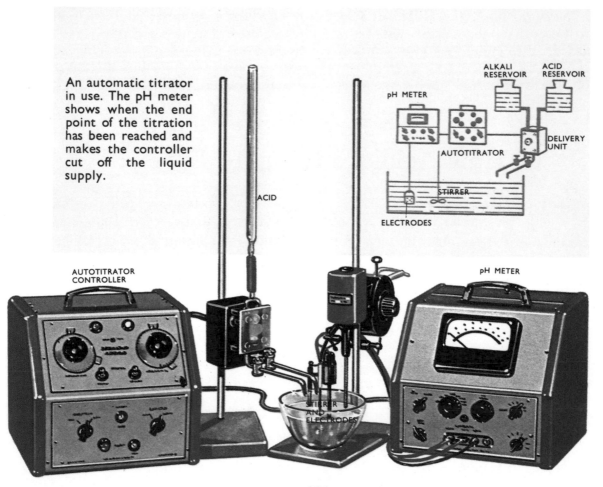

An automatic titrator in use. The pH meter shows when the end point of the titration has been reached and makes the controller cut off the liquid supply.

pH stands for potency of hydrogen ions or hydrogen ion concentration, usually of a watery solution. pH7 indicates a neutral solution. Anything below 7 will be acidic, and above it alkaline. Ordinary tap water is neutral. Most of its molecules are un-ionized, but just a few split up into hydrogen ions ($H^+$) and hydroxyl ions ($OH^-$). Because they are present in equal numbers the solution is neutral. There are $10^{-7}$ grams of hydrogen ions in a litre of tap water. The pH of tap water is 7, the pH of any neutral solution.

Hydrogen and hydroxyl ions behave in a kind of see-saw fashion. As one goes down, the other goes up. As the hydrogen ion concentration goes up, making a solution more acidic, the hydroxyl ion concentration goes down. It is impossible to increase one without decreasing the other. So the acidity or alkalinity of a solution can be described in terms of hydrogen ion concentration only.

If acid is added to tap water, the hydrogen ion content is increased. If it is increased from $10^{-7}$ to $10^{-5}$ gram ions per litre the pH becomes 5. When alkalis are added to water, the hydroxyl ion content shoots up and so the hydrogen ion concentration drops. If it drops to $10^{-10}$ gram ions per litre, the pH rises to 10.

But jam manufacturers using the pH meter are just interested in the quantity of sugar to be added. It is of no importance to them that there may be $10^{-5}$ grams of hydrogen ions per litre of the jam although this is, in fact, the information supplied by the meter. The meter is used indirectly to follow the reaction in the jam vat.

*titrations.* In a titration liquid is run from a burette to mix with another liquid in a flask placed underneath.

Some sort of reaction takes place between them. The aim is to discover the volume of liquid required to exactly complete the reaction. Indicators will show this by changing colour, but they are often grossly inaccurate and the colour changes may not be sharp enough. This is not true of the pH meter. There is usually an unmistakable sharp change in pH at the 'end point'.

Industrial and laboratory pH meters are basically the same. Two glass sheathed electrodes dip in the solution under the test. The glass membrane of one of these electrodes is actually responsible for detecting the pH of the solution. Industrial pH meters are usually part of a permanent installation and the electrodes occupy a very definite position in the tank of liquid. Because of this, they are often housed in a rigid stainless steel canister. As well as positioning the electrodes this also helps to protect them. Laboratory pH meters are not permanent fixtures. First the electrodes are dipped into one solution and then into another. Therefore, they need no housing. This does make them clearly visible, but because they are not protected the electrodes must be handled with more care.

## How the pH meter works

When a thin walled glass tube is dipped into a solution a small voltage is generated on the glass. The size of this voltage depends upon the pH of the surrounding solution – the higher the pH, the higher the voltage. This is always true provided there are no temperature variations. At room temperature an increase of 1 pH increases the voltage generated by 59 millivolts.

In other words, the glass acts as a generator whose performance depends on the pH. If the pH is low the voltage generated is also low. When the solution is more alkaline and has a higher pH the voltage generated across the glass membrane is also higher. Why does this happen? There is at the moment no proper explanation, but nevertheless, the behaviour of the glass is absolutely reliable and this fact is utilized by the pH meter.

# CHAPTER TWENTY-EIGHT

# Ion Measurements and Titrations

**W**HEN liquids conduct electricity there is a two-way traffic in ions. Positive ions move to the negatively charged cathode and negative ions to the positively charged anode. At the electrodes the ions lose their charges to form neutral atoms or molecules. So the ions, which were originally in solution, are released in the form of gases or layers of plated-out metal on the electrodes.

This process of *electrolysis* has many practical applications – the important electroplating industry is based on it, and the industrial separation of many chemicals – chlorine gas and aluminium amongst them – is carried out in large electrolytic cells.

To the scientist, the study of the properties of conducting solutions yields important information. An easily-measured quantity is the *elec-*

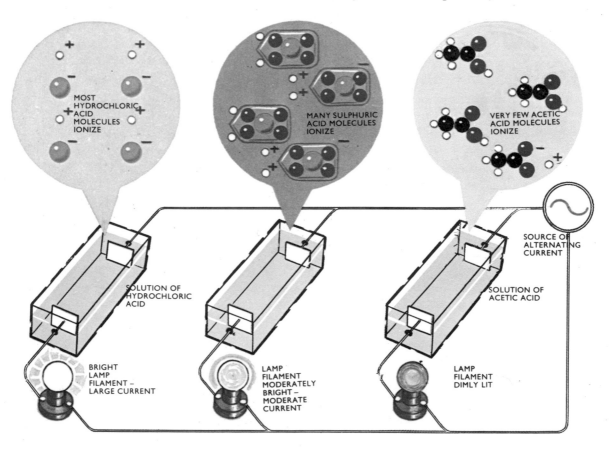

MOST HYDROCHLORIC ACID MOLECULES IONIZE

MANY SULPHURIC ACID MOLECULES IONIZE

VERY FEW ACETIC ACID MOLECULES IONIZE

SOURCE OF ALTERNATING CURRENT

SOLUTION OF HYDROCHLORIC ACID

SOLUTION OF ACETIC ACID

BRIGHT LAMP FILAMENT – LARGE CURRENT

LAMP FILAMENT MODERATELY BRIGHT – MODERATE CURRENT

LAMP FILAMENT DIMLY LIT

*In the three cells there are acids of equal concentration but different strengths. The cells are connected across a common mains supply but the three bulbs light up with different intensities. This shows that each cell carries a different current because the solutions contain different numbers of ions.*

PORTABLE
CONDUCTIVITY
PROBE

*A commercial conductivity meter in which a direct reading of conductivity is obtained. The portable conductivity cell is used as a 'probe' which may be inserted into a stationary volume of liquid, as in the illustration, or in a flowing liquid. Inside the cell a pair of parallel platinum electrodes are sealed.*

*trical conductivity* of a solution – this is a measure of the amount of electric charge that is pushed through the liquid (as a result of the two-way ion traffic) when a voltage difference is set up between the electrodes.

The conductivity values of different solutions are of interest to the chemist because they give a direct guide to the numbers and types of ions present in a solution, and this, in turn, provides information about the chemical nature of the compound dissolved in the solution.

This is easily demonstrated in a simple experiment. Solutions of hydrochloric, sulphuric and acetic acids are made up so that each has the same *normality* (this means that equal volumes of each solution would be neutralized by equal amounts of an alkali such as sodium hydroxide). Equal volumes of each acid solution

are poured into identical conductivity cells. These are glass cells in which identical pairs of metal electrodes have been sealed. The three cells are each placed in series with an identical electric light bulb and the three pairs of bulb and cell are all connected in *parallel* across the electricity mains. An alternating current passes through each cell and bulb, and the three bulbs light up. The lamp in series with the hydrochloric acid cell shines brightest of all, and the 'sulphuric acid' bulb is brighter than the bulb in series with the acetic acid. This can only mean that the current passing through each of the three cells is different, so the **number of ions available to carry charge to the electrodes is different in each cell.**

What is the significance of this? The number of free hydrogen ions present in an acid solution determines the

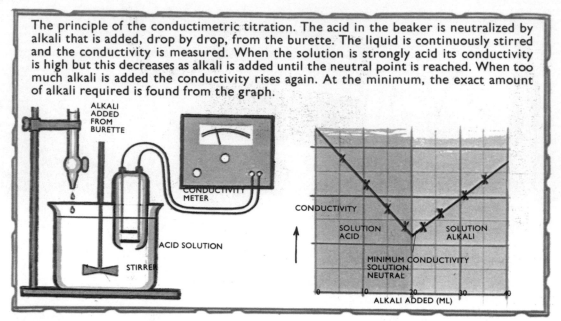

The principle of the conductimetric titration. The acid in the beaker is neutralized by alkali that is added, drop by drop, from the burette. The liquid is continuously stirred and the conductivity is measured. When the solution is strongly acid its conductivity is high but this decreases as alkali is added until the neutral point is reached. When too much alkali is added the conductivity rises again. At the minimum, the exact amount of alkali required is found from the graph.

*strength* of an acid, so the conductivity of an acid solution is a measure of its strength. (This is not to be confused with the *normality* or *concentration* of the solution – this is determined by the total number of acid molecules present.) The strength of an acid will determine the vigour of its reactions – the rate at which it will attack metals, for example.

When an acid is dissolved in water there is immediate *dissociation* into ions. Hydrochloric acid molecules ionize into hydrogen ($H^+$) ions and chloride ($Cl^-$) ions:

$$HCl \rightarrow H^+ + Cl^-.$$

The extent to which dissociation takes place determines the strength of the acid. In a strong acid such as hydrochloric acid 92% of the acid molecules dissociate into ions. In acetic acid, a weak acid, only 1% of the acid molecules dissociate. The electrical conductivity is obviously related to the strength of the acid because the hydrogen ions carry the greatest proportion of the charge through the solution.

Apart from providing information about the number of free ions in a solution, conductivity measurements also provide information about the type of ions that are free in solution. For example, part of the conductivity difference between acetic and hydrochloric acids is due to the different speeds that chloride ions and acetate ions have in solution. This is in addition to the fact that there are less of the acetate ions, anyway, because it is a weaker acid. More of the faster chloride ions reach the anode in a given time so a greater negative ion current is created. In solution, the total conductivity is due to the sum of the individual conductivities of the different types of ions present. This fact is used in a very important application of conductivity measurements – the *conductimetric titration.*

In an ordinary titration, to measure the concentration of an acid solution, a measured quantity of a neutralizing solution (alkali in this case) is added until the *end point* is reached. Then the hydrogen (acid) ions are completely neutralised by the hydroxyl (alkali) ions:

$$H^+ + OH^- \rightarrow H_2O$$

and a chemical indicator like litmus or phenolpthalein will change colour. In a conductimetric titration the conductivity of the solution is continuously measured. At first, when the solution is strongly acid, there are many hydrogen ions present and the conductivity is high. As alkali is added, the conductivity is lowered and reaches a minimum when the acid is completely neutralised. If more alkali is added, the conductivity increases again because there is an excess of hydroxyl ions.

Quantities of alkali are added from a burette and the solution is mixed before the conductivity is measured. The measured conductivity is plotted on a graph, against volume of alkali added, and the curve reaches a minimum for the volume of alkali needed for neutralisation.

Ideally, the numbers of free hydroxyl and hydrogen ions present is then very small indeed. The method provides an accurate way of determining end-points, and it is used in a number of titration reactions where chemical indicators are not satisfactory.

## Measuring Conductivity

The solution is poured into a glass conductivity cell in which a parallel pair of platinum electrodes is sealed. The conductivity ($K$) of a solution between plates of area ($A$) separated by distance ($D$) is given by $K = \dfrac{D}{RA}$, where $R$ is the measured electrical resistance between the plates.

It is not always practicable to find the conductivity of a solution from the dimensions of the cell and its measured resistance. Then, the resistance is compared with that obtained when the cell is filled with solution of known conductivity. The cell, filled with electrolyte is placed in a *bridge circuit* and its resistance is compared with that of a known resistor. In the bridge circuit, an *alternating current* is used so that gas is not given off at the electrodes – it would affect the measured conductivity.

In the *Kohlrausch bridge* circuit the value of resistance of the cell is 'matched' with that of the circuit resistance, using the bridge wire. (This is very much like using the Wheatstone bridge to measure a d.c. resistance.) When balance is achieved no sound is heard in a pair of earphones connected to the circuit.

## Applications

Conductimetric measurements are carried out in industry to determine the purity of water. Distilled water has a low conductivity (if really pure there is a low ionic concentration), so to test purity, conductivity meters are employed. The degree of purity of

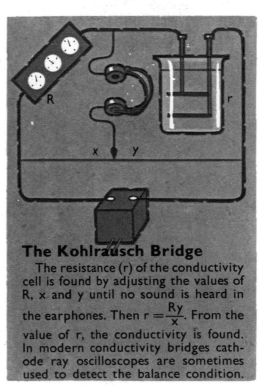

**The Kohlrausch Bridge**
The resistance (r) of the conductivity cell is found by adjusting the values of R, x and y until no sound is heard in the earphones. Then $r = \dfrac{Ry}{x}$. From the value of r, the conductivity is found. In modern conductivity bridges cathode ray oscilloscopes are sometimes used to detect the balance condition.

inflowing feed waters for industrial boilers must also be controlled to prevent scaling. Conductivity meters are used in this work as well. Specially constructed probe cells are available.

One interesting application of conductimetric titration is for measuring small moisture contents in liquid and solid materials. The method used is called a *Karl Fischer titration*.

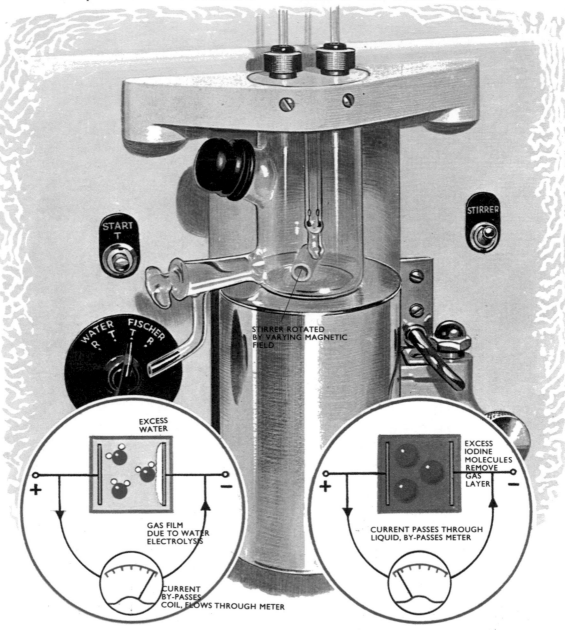

*Part of an automatic Karl Fischer titration apparatus, to which the reagent is added automatically. (Inset) When water is present a gas film is formed on the electrode and all the current passes through the meter. When there is an excess of iodine the film disappears and the reagent 'shunts' the meter producing zero reading. Volume of reagent added to produce zero reading gives an accurate value of moisture content.*

# Appendices

# A Pictorial Summary of Reactions in Chemistry

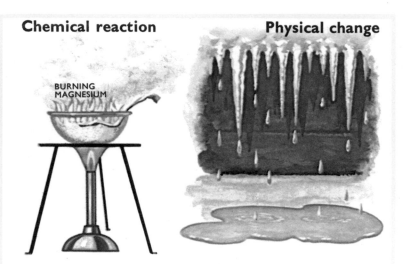

**Chemical reaction**

BURNING MAGNESIUM

**Physical change**

*Chemical reactions are changes in which some new compound is formed. If there is no new compound, then the change is not chemical but physical. For example when ice melts to form water, both the water and the ice are chemically the same. This is a physical change. When magnesium is heated it bursts into flame. White clouds of the newly formed compound, magnesium oxide, come off and more white oxide is left behind as an ash. This is a chemical change.*

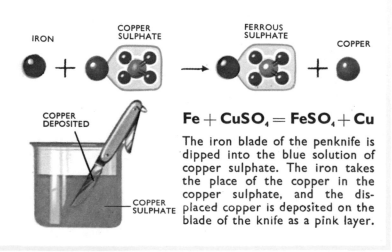

IRON

COPPER SULPHATE

FERROUS SULPHATE

COPPER

COPPER DEPOSITED

COPPER SULPHATE

$$Fe + CuSO_4 = FeSO_4 + Cu$$

The iron blade of the penknife is dipped into the blue solution of copper sulphate. The iron takes the place of the copper in the copper sulphate, and the displaced copper is deposited on the blade of the knife as a pink layer.

## Replacement Reactions
*Whenever someone is replaced in a team, another person takes his place and the original person moves out. This describes the behaviour of atoms in a replacement reaction. An atom (or group of atoms) takes the place of another atom (or group of atoms) in a compound.*

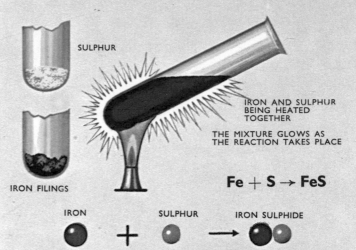

SULPHUR

IRON AND SULPHUR
BEING HEATED
TOGETHER

THE MIXTURE GLOWS AS
THE REACTION TAKES PLACE

IRON FILINGS

$$Fe + S \rightarrow FeS$$

IRON     SULPHUR     IRON SULPHIDE

When sulphur and powdered iron are heated in the correct proportions, *i.e.* so that there is one atom of sulphur present for every atom of iron, the new compound, iron sulphide, forms. A great deal of extra heat is given off by the reaction, making the inside of the tube glow. The iron sulphide formed is unaffected by a magnet, showing there is no iron left.

## Combination or Addition Reactions

*Of the many types of chemical reaction, the combination (or addition) reaction is the simplest. The reacting substances (either elements or compounds) combine, adding together to form a new chemical compound. There are no by-products of such a reaction. Only the new compound is formed.*

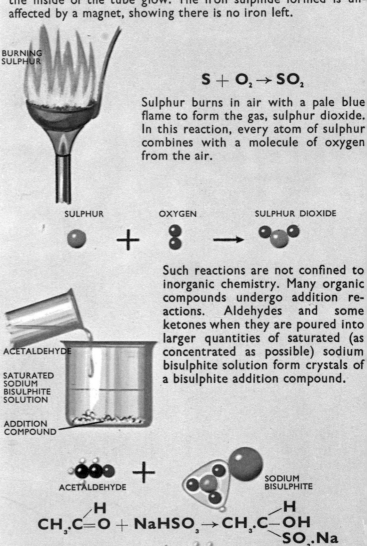

BURNING
SULPHUR

$$S + O_2 \rightarrow SO_2$$

Sulphur burns in air with a pale blue flame to form the gas, sulphur dioxide. In this reaction, every atom of sulphur combines with a molecule of oxygen from the air.

SULPHUR     OXYGEN     SULPHUR DIOXIDE

Such reactions are not confined to inorganic chemistry. Many organic compounds undergo addition reactions. Aldehydes and some ketones when they are poured into larger quantities of saturated (as concentrated as possible) sodium bisulphite solution form crystals of a bisulphite addition compound.

ACETALDEHYDE

SATURATED
SODIUM
BISULPHITE
SOLUTION

ADDITION
COMPOUND

ACETALDEHYDE     SODIUM BISULPHITE

$$CH_3.C{=}O + NaHSO_3 \rightarrow CH_3.C{-}OH$$

with H above and SO$_3$.Na below

ADDITION
COMPOUND

# Thermal decomposition

This simply means the splitting of a compound by the action of heat

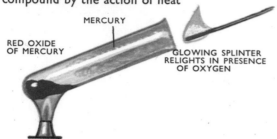

RED OXIDE OF MERCURY

MERCURY

GLOWING SPLINTER RELIGHTS IN PRESENCE OF OXYGEN

BUBBLES OF OXYGEN

HYDROGEN PEROXIDE

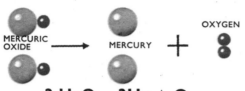

MERCURIC OXIDE

MERCURY

OXYGEN

$$2\,HgO \rightarrow 2Hg + O_2$$

Heat splits up the red oxide of mercury into its elements. Small grey beads of mercury condense on the cool sides of the test tube. The colourless oxygen gas given off relights a glowing wooden splinter after the flame has been blown out.

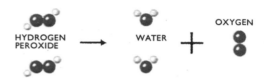

HYDROGEN PEROXIDE

WATER

OXYGEN

$$2H_2O_2 \rightarrow 2H_2O + O_2$$

When peroxide (hydrogen peroxide) is heated, bubbles of gas rise to the surface. These are bubbles of oxygen. The peroxide has been split into oxygen and water.

POTASSIUM CHLORATE AND MANGANESE DIOXIDE

OXYGEN

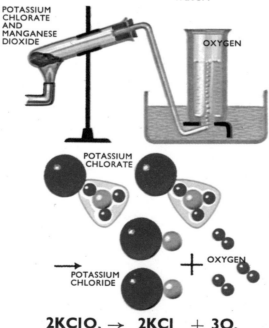

POTASSIUM CHLORATE

POTASSIUM CHLORIDE

OXYGEN

$$2KClO_3 \rightarrow 2KCl + 3O_2$$

On heating, potassium chlorate decomposes into potassium chloride and oxygen. Some manganese dioxide is mixed with the potassium chlorate as a catalyst to speed up the reaction.

## Dehydration

Dehydration is a chemical reaction in which a substance is decomposed and water is one of the products. The molecule may be completely disrupted or it may just have loosely bound water driven off.

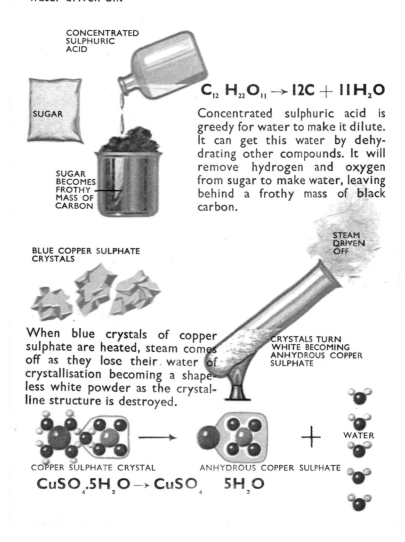

CONCENTRATED SULPHURIC ACID

SUGAR

SUGAR BECOMES FROTHY MASS OF CARBON

$$C_{12}H_{22}O_{11} \rightarrow 12C + 11H_2O$$

Concentrated sulphuric acid is greedy for water to make it dilute. It can get this water by dehydrating other compounds. It will remove hydrogen and oxygen from sugar to make water, leaving behind a frothy mass of black carbon.

BLUE COPPER SULPHATE CRYSTALS

STEAM DRIVEN OFF

When blue crystals of copper sulphate are heated, steam comes off as they lose their water of crystallisation becoming a shapeless white powder as the crystalline structure is destroyed.

CRYSTALS TURN WHITE BECOMING ANHYDROUS COPPER SULPHATE

COPPER SULPHATE CRYSTAL

ANHYDROUS COPPER SULPHATE

WATER

$$CuSO_4.5H_2O \rightarrow CuSO_4 \quad 5H_2O$$

# Combustion

Combustion is another word for burning. Any substance that can be set on fire by heating is combustible. Oxygen (which forms part of the air) is essential for combustion as the burning substance combines with oxygen to form the oxide. Heat is given out by this reaction.

*Rapid combustion.* In a car cylinder, petrol vapour and air react explosively when ignited by a spark.

*Slow combustion.* The rusting of iron is an example of slow combustion. As the heat of reaction is given out over such a long period of time, a piece of rusty iron does not feel hot.

$$4Fe + 3O_2 \rightarrow 2Fe_2O_3$$

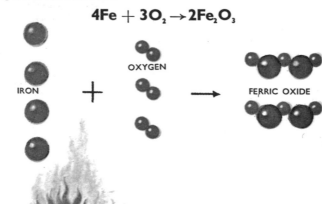

IRON + OXYGEN → FERRIC OXIDE

This bonfire burns at a rate intermediate between slow and rapid. This is ordinary combustion.

## Double decomposition

The Browns are dancing together; so are the Smiths. In the next dance, Mr. Brown dances with Mrs. Smith and Mr. Smith dances with Mrs. Brown. They have changed partners, behaving very similarly to two compounds undergoing double decomposition. This is a chemical reaction in which two metallic radicles exchange their acid radicle partners.

Double decomposition is often used to prepare an insoluble salt from solutions of two soluble salts. On mixing, the metallic radicle exchanges its acid radicle partner and the insoluble salt is precipitated.

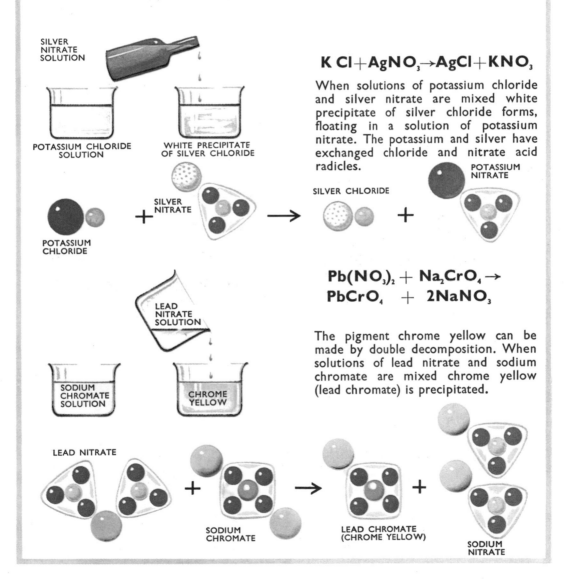

**K Cl + AgNO₃ → AgCl + KNO₃**

When solutions of potassium chloride and silver nitrate are mixed white precipitate of silver chloride forms, floating in a solution of potassium nitrate. The potassium and silver have exchanged chloride and nitrate acid radicles.

**Pb(NO₃)₂ + Na₂CrO₄ → PbCrO₄ + 2NaNO₃**

The pigment chrome yellow can be made by double decomposition. When solutions of lead nitrate and sodium chromate are mixed chrome yellow (lead chromate) is precipitated.

## Oxidation and reduction

Oxidation is a chemical reaction in which a substance gains oxygen. In burning, the oxygen is gained from the air but in other oxidation reactions it is gained at the expense of another chemical compound known as an oxidizing agent. The oxidizing agent is itself *reduced*, *i.e.* it loses oxygen.

These were the original definitions of oxidation and reduction, but now they have been extended to include reactions where oxygen is not involved. Whenever a ferrous salt (valency 2) is converted to its higher valency state of 3 to become a ferric salt, it is oxidized. Here electrons are lost. If the reverse takes place and a salt of lower valency is formed, then a reduction has taken place. Electrons are gained by the reduced compound.

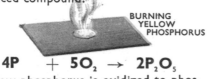

BURNING YELLOW PHOSPHORUS

$$4P + 5O_2 \rightarrow 2P_2O_5$$

Yellow phosphorus is oxidized to phosphorus pentoxide by the oxygen in the air.

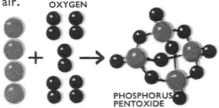

OXYGEN

PHOSPHORUS

PHOSPHORUS PENTOXIDE

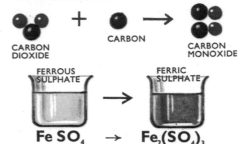

$$CO_2 + C \rightarrow 2CO$$

Red hot carbon reduces carbon dioxide to carbon monoxide. In doing so, the carbon gains oxygen and is oxidized to carbon monoxide.

CARBON DIOXIDE + CARBON → CARBON MONOXIDE

FERROUS SULPHATE → FERRIC SULPHATE

$$Fe SO_4 \rightarrow Fe_2(SO_4)_3$$

Exposure to the air gradually oxidizes the green solution of ferrous sulphate (valency of ferrous iron 2) to brown ferric sulphate (valency of ferric iron 3).

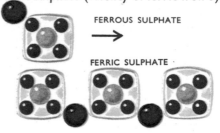

FERROUS SULPHATE →

FERRIC SULPHATE

## Reversible reactions

A reversible reaction is one which can proceed in either direction according to the conditions. For example, if a stream of hydrogen is passed over hot magnetic iron oxide ($Fe_3O_4$) the oxide is reduced (*i.e.* loses its oxygen) to metallic iron and some of the hydrogen is oxidized to steam (*i.e.* joins with the released oxygen). But, if steam is blown over iron filings, exactly the reverse takes place. The iron is oxidized to magnetic iron oxide and some steam is reduced to hydrogen.

$$Fe_3O_4 + 4H_2 \rightarrow 3Fe + 4H_2O \qquad 3Fe + 4H_2O \rightarrow Fe_3O_4 + 4H_2$$

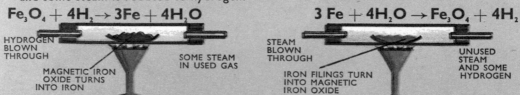

HYDROGEN BLOWN THROUGH

MAGNETIC IRON OXIDE TURNS INTO IRON

SOME STEAM IN USED GAS

STEAM BLOWN THROUGH

IRON FILINGS TURN INTO MAGNETIC IRON OXIDE

UNUSED STEAM AND SOME HYDROGEN

Incidentally, if iron filings were heated with steam in a closed container, only part of the iron would be converted to the oxide, after which there would appear to be no further change. A state of *equilibrium* would be arrived at. As fast as iron was converted to oxide, it would be reconverted back again.

$$3Fe + 4H_2O \leftrightarrows Fe_3O_4 + 4H_2$$

arrows show reaction proceeding in both directions

If the hydrogen were to be removed as fast as it were formed, all the iron would be changed to oxide in an attempt to make up the hydrogen deficiency.

## Electrolysis

Electrolysis occurs when chemical compounds are decomposed by the passage of an electric current.

Compounds can be classified in two groups – electrolytes and non-electrolytes. An electrolyte will conduct an electric current and in doing so will be split up by that current. Salts are electrolytes, whether in solution or in the molten state.

Substances such as sugar and paraffin (both are organic carbon-containing compounds) are incapable of conducting electric currents, nor are they decomposed by them. These are non-electrolytes.

## Electrolysis of molten sodium chloride

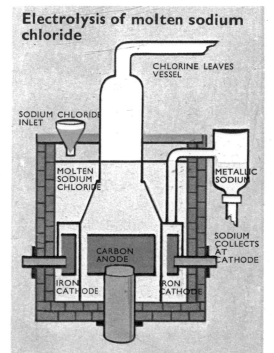

Molten, dry sodium chloride, common salt, is split up into the elements sodium and chlorine by passing an electric current through it. Sodium collects at the cathode and chlorine gas bubbles off at the anode. This reaction takes place in the Downs cell in which sodium and chlorine are produced on a commercial scale by electrolysing molten sodium chloride.

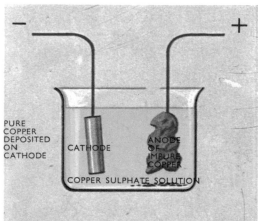

Electrolysis is used for purifying copper. The pure copper is deposited on the cathode; impurities are not.

## Hydrolysis

Hydrolysis occurs when double decomposition takes place between a salt and water. This is the reverse of neutralization where a salt and water are the end products. For example, water *hydrolyses* the unstable salt, aluminium chloride, to give an acidic solution. The hydroxyl group of water and the chloride of aluminium chloride change places to form aluminium hydroxide and the acid, hydrochloric acid.

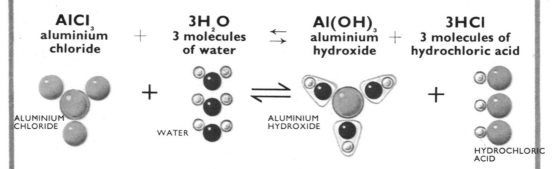

$AlCl_3$
**aluminium chloride**
$+$
$3H_2O$
**3 molecules of water**
$\rightleftharpoons$
$Al(OH)_3$
**aluminium hydroxide**
$+$
$3HCl$
**3 molecules of hydrochloric acid**

ALUMINIUM CHLORIDE
WATER
ALUMINIUM HYDROXIDE
HYDROCHLORIC ACID

As in all hydrolyses, this reaction is never completed. Not all the aluminium chloride becomes aluminium hydroxide, for the reaction is reversible. A state of equilibrium is reached where there is a certain amount of aluminium chloride, water, aluminium hydroxide and hydrochloric acid. As fast as the aluminium chloride reacts with water, the work is undone by the reverse reaction taking place. It is a bit like trying to move some things to the opposite side of the room while someone working at the same speed carries them back again. The reverse arrows in the equation show that the reaction is taking place in both directions.

# Neutralization

Neutralization is a reaction between any acid and any base to form a salt and water.

This is a special form of double decomposition. The two compounds change partners. The hydrogen of the acid joins with the oxide or hydroxyl (—OH) group of the base to form water. The salt is formed from the other radicles.

$$NaOH + HCl \rightarrow NaCl + H_2O$$
$$\text{base} + \text{acid} \rightarrow \text{salt} + \text{water}$$

The alkali, caustic soda, will neutralize hydrochloric acid. The two are mixed in the correct proportions so that the solution is neutral (neither acid nor basic). This is shown by the purple colour of the litmus test paper. Evaporation of the water leaves ordinary common salt.

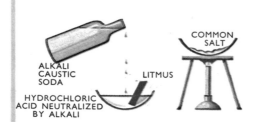

ALKALI CAUSTIC SODA

COMMON SALT

LITMUS

HYDROCHLORIC ACID NEUTRALIZED BY ALKALI

CAUSTIC SODA

HYDROCHLORIC ACID

SODIUM CHLORIDE

WATER

COPPER OXIDE

$$H_2SO_4 + CuO \rightarrow CuSO_4 + H_2O$$
$$\text{acid} + \text{base} \rightarrow \text{salt} + \text{water}$$

The base, black copper oxide, neutralizes dilute sulphuric acid to form the blue salt, copper sulphate, and water.

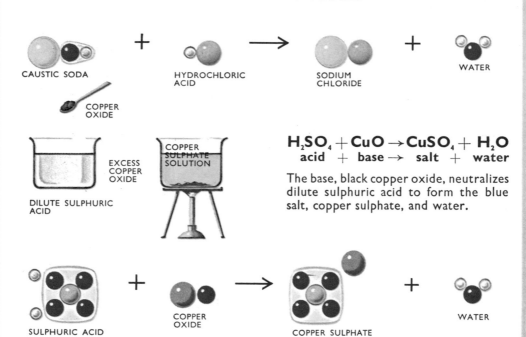

EXCESS COPPER OXIDE

DILUTE SULPHURIC ACID

COPPER SULPHATE SOLUTION

SULPHURIC ACID

COPPER OXIDE

COPPER SULPHATE

WATER

# Making Gases in the Laboratory

## Oxygen, O₂

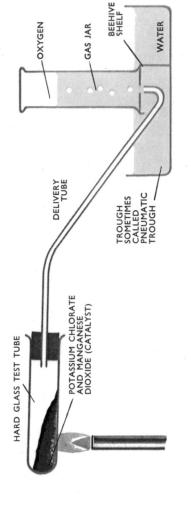

Oxygen is a colourless, odourless gas which is slightly soluble in water. About one fifth of the atmosphere consists of oxygen (the other main constituent is nitrogen). The element oxygen, or compounds containing oxygen, are essential to all forms of life. Animals and birds obtain oxygen from the air, while fish are supplied by oxygen dissolved in the water. Oxides are compounds of oxygen with various other elements. One way in which they may be formed is to burn the elements (e.g. sulphur, magnesium) in oxygen. Substances which only smoulder in air, burst into flame when put into a jar of oxygen.

$$2KClO_3 = 2KCl + 3O_2$$

potassium chlorate · potassium chloride · oxygen

One way to prepare oxygen is to heat potassium chlorate crystals with which black manganese dioxide powder has been mixed. The potassium chlorate decomposes – oxygen is set free and potassium choride is left behind in the hard glass test tube. The manganese dioxide acts as a *catalyst* – it reduces the temperature at which the potassium chlorate decomposes.

## Hydrogen, H₂

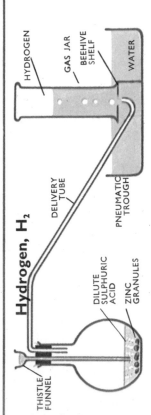

Hydrogen is a colourless, odourless gas which is insoluble in water. It is much less dense than air (it is the lightest gas known) and may be 'poured' upwards. Hydrogen burns in air with a blue flame to form water. Mixtures, in certain proportions, of air (or oxygen) and hydrogen burn with explosive violence, so that care must always be taken when preparing hydrogen to ensure that all the air has been driven out of the apparatus before tests are carried out on the sample. As well as combining directly with oxygen, hydrogen will also remove the oxygen from metallic oxides e.g. litharge (lead monoxide, PbO). Water is formed at the same time as the oxide is *reduced* to the metal.

$$Zn + H_2SO_4 = ZnSO_4 + H_2$$

zinc · sulphuric acid · zinc sulphate · hydrogen

Of the many ways by which hydrogen may be made in the laboratory, the one which is used most frequently is that in which a dilute acid reacts with a metal. The most convenient combination of reactants are zinc and dilute sulphuric acid. (Nitric acid is not suitable since there is a tendency for oxides of nitrogen to be formed.)

## Nitrogen, N₂

Nitrogen is a colourless, odourless gas which is almost insoluble in water. Nitrogen makes up about four-fifths of the gas in the atmosphere. Nitrogen does not burn, and if a burning substance is plunged into this gas the flames are quickly extinguished. Exceptionally, burning magnesium ribbon continues to burn feebly and magnesium nitride is formed. Few nitrogen compounds can be formed by direct action between nitrogen and other elements. Nevertheless there are many nitrogen-containing compounds, including a large number of organic compounds, e.g. proteins, which are essential to life.

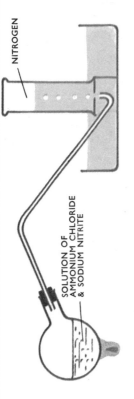

AMMONIUM CHLORIDE

SODIUM NITRITE

SODIUM CHLORIDE

WATER

NITROGEN

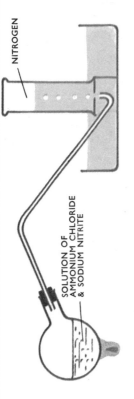

NITROGEN

SOLUTION OF AMMONIUM CHLORIDE & SODIUM NITRITE

Although nitrogen can be obtained from the air after oxygen and carbon dioxide have been removed, this residue also contains traces of the inert gases as impurity. A purer product may be made by gently warming a strong solution of ammonium chloride and sodium nitrite.

$$NH_4Cl + NaNO_2 = NaCl + 2H_2O + N_2$$

ammonium chloride | sodium nitrite | sodium chloride | water | nitrogen

In a double decomposition reaction sodium chloride and ammonium nitrite are formed, but the latter compound splits up almost as soon as it is formed to yield nitrogen and water.

## Ammonia, NH₃

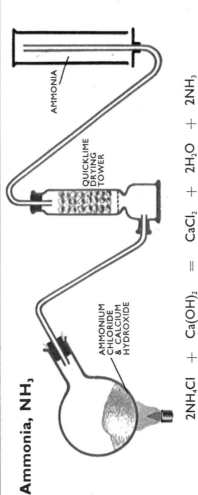

AMMONIA

QUICKLIME DRYING TOWER

AMMONIUM CHLORIDE & CALCIUM HYDROXIDE

Ammonia is a colourless gas with a distinctive pungent odour. It is very soluble in water. The density of ammonia is rather less than that of air, so that it can be 'poured' upwards. Ammonia does not burn in air, neither do other substances continue to burn in ammonia. However, in oxygen ammonia burns with a greenish flame. A solution of ammonia in water is weakly alkaline – it turns red litmus blue – and contains some ammonium hydroxide. Ammonia reacts with acids to form the ammonium series of salts.

$$2NH_4Cl + Ca(OH)_2 = CaCl_2 + 2H_2O + 2NH_3$$

ammonium chloride | calcium hydroxide | calcium chloride | water | ammonia

The usual method for making ammonia gas on a small scale is to mix together powdered calcium hydroxide (slaked lime) and powdered ammonium chloride, and then heat the dry mixture. Ammonia gas and water vapour are given off leaving calcium chloride behind. The gas is dried by passing it up a tower containing quicklime.

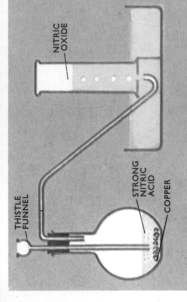

NITROUS OXIDE

WARM WATER

AMMONIUM SULPHATE & SODIUM NITRATE

## Nitrous Oxide, N₂O

Nitrous oxide is a colourless gas with a sweet smell. It is soluble in cold water. It does not burn, but on heating the gas is quite easily decomposed into nitrogen and oxygen. Since the decomposition mixture is richer in oxygen than the air, substances which are already burning in air will burn more brightly in nitrous oxide. Mixed with oxygen, nitrous oxide is used as a general anaesthetic for dentistry and surgery.

$$(NH_4)_2SO_4 + 2NaNO_3 = Na_2SO_4 + 4H_2O + 2N_2O$$
ammonium sulphate   sodium nitrate   sodium sulphate   water   nitrous oxide

Nitrous oxide is usually prepared by cautiously heating together a mixture of ammonium sulphate and sodium nitrate. By a double decomposition reaction sodium sulphate and ammonium nitrate are formed. The latter compound then decomposes to yield nitrous oxide and water. (This method is preferable to heating ammonium nitrate alone, since this compound tends to explode.) The gas is often collected over warm water as it is soluble in cold.

## Nitrogen Dioxide, NO₂

Nitrogen dioxide, which is also called nitrogen peroxide, is a red-brown gas with an irritating smell. The gas is poisonous. It does not burn, and extinguishes the flames of almost all burning substances. In a good freezing mixture nitrogen dioxide condenses to give a yellow liquid (boiling point 22°C), after further cooling almost colourless crystals (melting point −9°C) are obtained. In the liquid and solid states pairs of nitrogen dioxide molecules combine (associate) to produce single molecules of nitrogen tetroxide (N₂O₄). Nitrogen dioxide is an acidic oxide – it dissolves in water forming a mixture of nitrous and nitric acids and reacts with sodium hydroxide solution to give sodium nitrite and sodium nitrate. It is used as the 'oxygen carrier' in the manufacture of sulphuric acid by the lead chamber process.

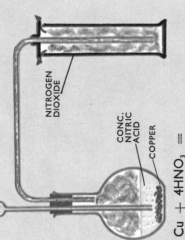

NITROGEN DIOXIDE

CONC. NITRIC ACID

COPPER

$$Cu + 4HNO_3 = Cu(NO_3)_2 + 2H_2O + 2NO_2$$
copper   nitric acid   cupric nitrate   water   nitrogen dioxide

Nitrogen dioxide is usually made in the laboratory by the action in the cold of concentrated nitric acid on copper turnings. By using the stronger acid the reducing action is not so great as that produced by using the slightly weaker acid.

---

THISTLE FUNNEL

NITRIC OXIDE

STRONG NITRIC ACID

COPPER

$$3Cu + 8HNO_3 = 3Cu(NO_3)_2 + 4H_2O + 2NO$$
copper   nitric acid   cupric nitrate   water   nitric oxide

Nitric oxide may be made by the reaction between copper turnings and strong nitric acid (a mixture of equal parts of water and concentrated acid). Although cupric nitrate is formed, the copper also serves to reduce some of the nitric acid to nitric oxide.

## Nitric Oxide, NO

Nitric oxide is a colourless gas which is insoluble in water. It does not burn, and the flame of almost any burning substance is extinguished if it is put into the gas. However, the heat given out by strongly burning phosphorus may be sufficient to decompose the gas, in which case burning will continue. In the cold, nitric oxide combines with oxygen to yield nitrogen dioxide. Thus, as soon as nitric oxide comes into contact with air or oxygen, brown fumes of nitrogen dioxide are observed. An unstable brown compound is formed when nitric oxide is passed into an acidified solution of ferrous sulphate. This is the same compound that is formed in the brown ring test for nitrates.

# Chlorine, Cl₂

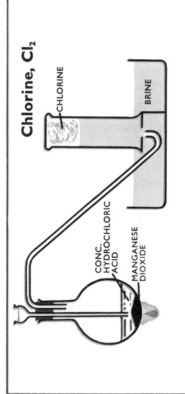

CHLORINE

CONC. HYDROCHLORIC ACID

MANGANESE DIOXIDE

BRINE

$$MnO_2 + 4HCl = MnCl_2 + 2H_2O + Cl_2$$

manganese   hydrochloric    manganous    water    chlorine
dioxide     acid         chloride

Chlorine may be prepared by the oxidation of hydrochloric acid – hydrogen ions are oxidized to water thus releasing the free element chlorine. The usual way of bringing about the reduction is to heat manganese dioxide with concentrated hydrochloric acid. Although the gas is soluble in water, it may be collected over a strong solution of sodium chloride. Chlorine is also obtained by the electrolysis of sodium chloride solution using carbon electrodes. Chlorine is liberated at the anode (positive electrode) while hydrogen is set free at the cathode (negative electrode) leaving an excess of OH⁻ ions. With Na⁺ ions attracted to the cathode this is equivalent to a solution of sodium hydroxide.

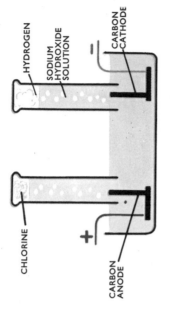

HYDROGEN

SODIUM HYDROXIDE SOLUTION

CARBON CATHODE

CHLORINE

CARBON ANODE

**ELECTROLYSIS OF BRINE**

Chlorine is a yellowish green gas with a choking odour. It is very poisonous and was the poison gas of World War I. Chlorine is more than twice as dense as air and is quite soluble in water. Chlorine does not burn but as it is a very reactive substance, a number of elements, both metals and non-metals (e.g. sodium, phosphorus) combine directly with chlorine. The heat of the reaction is often sufficient for the other elements to take fire in the chlorine gas. In some reactions chlorine acts as an oxidizing agent by removing hydrogen from compounds. The hydrogen combines with the chlorine to yield hydrogen chloride. The action of chlorine as a bleaching agent is but one example of its oxidizing properties.

## Hydrogen Chloride, HCl

Hydrogen chloride is a colourless gas with a distinctive pungent odour. In moist air it forms a white mist. It is very soluble in water, hence the need to collect it by upward displacement of air. A solution of hydrogen chloride in water turns blue litmus red – it is an acid called hydrochloric acid that has been formed. Hydrogen chloride does not burn and the flames of any burning substance are extinguished if put in the gas. Hydrogen chloride is very reactive and forms chlorides by replacement reactions with the more reactive metals. If it is mixed with ammonia gas, a white cloud of ammonium chloride particles is formed.

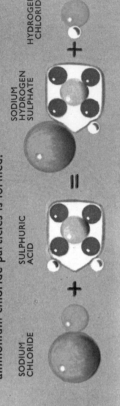

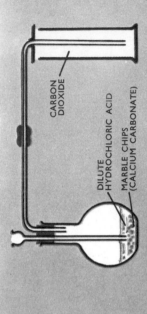

In the laboratory the gas hydrogen chloride is prepared by the action of concentrated sulphuric acid on a metallic chloride. Normally sodium chloride is used as it is cheap and readily available. After a fairly vigorous reaction in the cold a further supply of the gas may be obtained by heating the flask.

$$NaCl + H_2SO_4 = NaHSO_4 + HCl$$

sodium chloride · sulphuric acid · sodium hydrogen sulphate · hydrogen chloride

## Carbon Dioxide, CO₂

Carbon dioxide is a colourless gas with hardly any odour. It is slightly soluble in water under normal atmospheric pressure, but under higher pressures a larger quantity of the gas will dissolve. Carbon dioxide is rather denser than air so it can be poured from one container to another in much the same way as water. Carbon dioxide does not burn and the flames of any burning objects are rapidly extinguished when put into the gas. On account of this and the high density of the gas, it is used in fire extinguishers. The heat of burning magnesium, however, is sufficient to reduce the gas to carbon while the magnesium is oxidized to magnesium oxide. When the gas is passed into lime water (a weak solution of calcium hydroxide in water) fine grains of white calcium carbonate are observed. This is used as a test for carbon dioxide. A solution of carbon dioxide in water turns the colour of blue litmus to dull red. This is because some of the carbon dioxide has reacted with the water to yield unstable carbonic acid.

Carbon dioxide may conveniently be prepared by the action of an acid on a carbonate. The usual combination is dilute hydrochloric acid and calcium carbonate in the form of marble or limestone. The reaction proceeds satisfactorily in the cold. As the gas is soluble in water and denser than air it is collected by upward displacement of air (i.e. the gas pushes the air up and out of the jar).

$$CaCO_3 + 2HCl = CaCl_2 + H_2O + CO_2$$

calcium carbonate · hydrochloric acid · calcium chloride · water · carbon dioxide

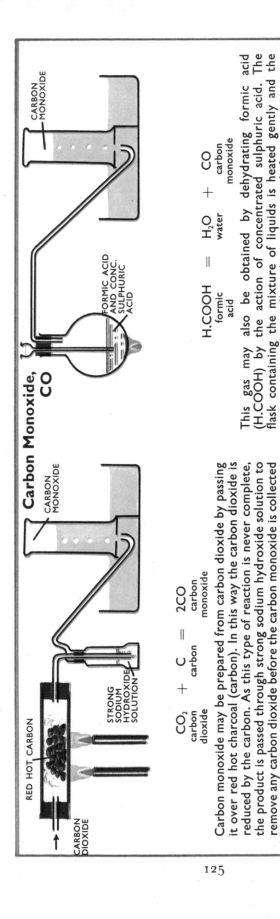

# Carbon Monoxide, CO

CARBON MONOXIDE

CARBON MONOXIDE

CARBON DIOXIDE

RED HOT CARBON

STRONG SODIUM HYDROXIDE SOLUTION

$$CO_2 + C = 2CO$$
carbon dioxide  carbon  carbon monoxide

Carbon monoxide may be prepared from carbon dioxide by passing it over red hot charcoal (carbon). In this way the carbon dioxide is reduced by the carbon. As this type of reaction is never complete, the product is passed through strong sodium hydroxide solution to remove any carbon dioxide before the carbon monoxide is collected over water.

FORMIC ACID AND CONC. SULPHURIC ACID

$$H.COOH = H_2O + CO$$
formic acid  water  carbon monoxide

This gas may also be obtained by dehydrating formic acid (H.COOH) by the action of concentrated sulphuric acid. The flask containing the mixture of liquids is heated gently and the carbon monoxide is collected over water as before.

Carbon monoxide is a colourless odourless gas which is insoluble in water. It is very poisonous forming as it does the very stable bright red compound carboxyhaemoglobin with the haemoglobin in the blood. Carbon monoxide burns in air with a blue flame and this reaction gives out a moderate quantity of heat. It is a constituent of coal gas. As carbon monoxide readily combines with oxygen it finds use as a reducing agent, particularly in the extraction of metals (e.g. lead) from their oxides.

## Hydrogen Sulphide, H₂S

$$FeS + 2HCl = FeCl_2 + H_2S$$

$$\text{ferrous} \quad \text{hydrochloric} \quad \text{ferrous} \quad \text{hydrogen}$$
$$\text{sulphide} \quad \text{acid} \quad \text{chloride} \quad \text{sulphide}$$

Hydrogen sulphide may conveniently be prepared in the laboratory by the action in the cold of dilute hydrochloric acid on ferrous sulphide. As the gas is soluble in cold water it may be collected by upward displacement of air or over warm water.

Hydrogen sulphide is a colourless gas with a distinctive odour. The odour associated with bad eggs is caused by the breakdown of organic sulphur compounds to yield this gas. It is very poisonous. It burns in air with a pale blue flame — sulphur dioxide and water are formed. Hydrogen sulphide is soluble in water and the solution is slightly acidic. Hydrogen sulphide neutralizes alkalis to form salts known as *sulphides*. Double decomposition takes place if the gas is bubbled into solutions of salts of certain metals. Many sulphides are insoluble and have distinctive colours. As hydrogen sulphide is easily oxidized it acts as a *reducing* agent in a number of reactions.

HYDROGEN SULPHIDE

DILUTE HYDROCHLORIC ACID

FERROUS SULPHIDE

FERROUS SULPHIDE + HYDROCHLORIC ACID = FERROUS CHLORIDE + HYDROGEN SULPHIDE

126

## Sulphur Dioxide, SO₂

$$Cu + 2H_2SO_4 = CuSO_4 + 2H_2O + SO_2$$

$$\text{copper} \quad \text{sulphuric} \quad \text{cupric} \quad \text{water} \quad \text{sulphur}$$
$$\text{acid} \quad \text{sulphate} \quad \text{dioxide}$$

Generally when sulphur dioxide is required in the laboratory, it is obtained by heating copper turnings in concentrated sulphuric acid. Some of the acid is used in forming copper sulphate, but the rest of the acid is reduced to sulphur dioxide, while the hydrogen ions are oxidized to yield water.

Sulphur dioxide is a colourless gas with a distinctive pungent odour. The gas is much denser than air so is collected by upward displacement of air. It is soluble in water and the solution contains some sulphurous acid. If passed into a solution of sodium hydroxide a mixture of sodium bisulphite and sodium sulphite is formed. Sulphur dioxide acts as a reducing agent in certain reactions and is itself oxidized by being converted to sulphur trioxide or a sulphate. This is, in fact, the principle behind the lead chamber process for the manufacture of sulphuric acid. On account of its reducing properties sulphur dioxide can be used for bleaching. Although sulphur dioxide does not burn, powdered magnesium will burn in it — sulphur and magnesium oxide are formed. In this reaction sulphur dioxide acts as an *oxidizing* agent.

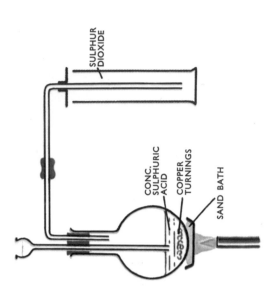

SULPHUR DIOXIDE

CONC. SULPHURIC ACID

COPPER TURNINGS

SAND BATH

# Index